PRACTICAL

METAL PLATE WORK

PAUL N. HASLUCK

reprinted by Lindsay Publications Inc

PRACTICAL METAL PLATE WORK

by Paul N. Hasluck

Originally published by
David McKay, Publisher
Philadelphia
1907

Reprinted by
Lindsay Publications Inc
Bradley IL 60915

ISBN 1-55918-159-1

1 2 3 4 5 6 7 8 9 0

1995

PRACTICAL
METAL PLATE WORK

WITH NUMEROUS ENGRAVINGS AND DIAGRAMS

EDITED BY

PAUL N. HASLUCK

HONOURS MEDALLIST IN TECHNOLOGY
EDITOR OF "WORK" AND "BUILDING WORLD"
AUTHOR OF "HANDYBOOKS FOR HANDICRAFTS," ETC. ETC.

PHILADELPHIA

DAVID McKAY, Publisher

610, *SOUTH WASHINGTON SQUARE*

1907

WARNING

Remember that the materials and methods described here are from another era. Workers were less safety conscious then, and some methods may be downright dangerous. Be careful! Use good solid judgement in your work, and think ahead. Lindsay Publications Inc. has not tested these methods and materials and does not endorse them. Our job is merely to pass along to you information from another era. Safety is your responsibility.

Write for a complete catalog of unusual books available from:

Lindsay Publications Inc
PO Box 12
Bradley IL 60915-0012

PREFACE.

PRACTICAL METAL PLATE WORK contains, in a form convenient for everyday use, a comprehensive digest of matter contributed by experienced craftsmen, scattered over the columns of WORK, one of the weekly journals it is my fortune to edit, and supplies concise information on the general principles and practice of the arts on which it treats.

In preparing for publication in book form the mass of relevant matter contained in the volumes of WORK, much of it necessarily had to be re-arranged and re-written. The greater portion of the matter relating to geometry as applied to patterns for articles formed of sheet metal was written by Mr. W. H. Bennett, Instructor in Metal Plate Work at the Regent Street Polytechnic, and he has also kindly revised the whole of the proofs of the present volume. A portion of the matter is quite new, having been written especially for this volume.

Readers who may desire additional information respecting special details of the matters dealt with in this book, or instruction on kindred subjects, should address a question to WORK, so that it may be answered in the columns of that journal.

P. N. HASLUCK.

CONTENTS.

LIST OF ILLUSTRATIONS.

PRACTICAL
METAL PLATE WORK.

CHAPTER I.

MATERIALS USED IN METAL PLATE WORK.

THE first chapter of a practical treatise on metal plate work may appropriately have as its subject the material which the sheet metal worker is called upon to manipulate. Chemists have divided the elements into two groups, metals and non-metals; but it is difficult to draw a sharp distinction that shall divide these two, as certain elements partake of the character of both groups. Obviously, the sheet metal worker has only to deal with those metals, pure and mixed, that are available for use in plates, and so the present object will be served by applying the term metal in its well-known, popular sense. Familiar metallic substances are gold, silver, iron, etc., and mixed metals are brass, bronze, steel (iron containing carbon), etc. Many metals not mentioned here are so rare that they are not known out of the laboratory and have no practical use in the arts.

The particular characteristic of a metal which makes it distinct from other inorganic productions is metallic lustre, and the following common properties and qualities distinguish the various metals. *Specific gravity*, which means the ratio of the weight of the metal to the weight of an equal bulk of water; thus 11·4, the specific gravity of lead, expresses the fact that, bulk for bulk, lead is 11·4 times heavier than water. *Fusibility*, which means capable of being melted or liquefied by heat; metals that melt at a low temperature are termed fusible, those that require great heat being known as refractory. *Ductility*, which means capable of being drawn into wire, the greater the ductility the finer the wire. *Malleability*, which means capable of being extended or shaped by being beaten with a hammer, or formed into thin sheets by the pressure of rollers. *Tenacity,* or cohesion, which means the holding together of the molecules, causing toughness as opposed to brittleness. *Hardness,* which means the capacity of one substance to scratch another or to be itself scratched. *Elasticity,* which means the inherent springiness by which a substance recovers its former shape or size after the removal of some external force that tends either to compress or elongate.

The chief distinguishing characteristics of the metals may be most readily estimated and compared when shown in tabular form, and so the following table has been prepared : it includes all those metals used in plates in common practice, though it must be remembered that the use of many metals which otherwise are very desirable for the purpose, is prohibited on account of their great cost.

NAME OF METAL OR ALLOY.	Symbol.	Specific Gravity.	Melting Point.		Relative Ductility.	Relative Malleability.	Relative Tenacity.
			*F.	†C.			
Aluminium ...	Al.	2·56	‡1050°	565·5°	6	5	9
Antimony ...	Sb.	6·7	810°	432·2°	—	—	—
Bismuth ...	Bi.	9·9	500°	260°	—	—	—
Brass ... ... Bronze	}	Greatly varies with composition.					
Copper	Cu.	8·9	2000°	1093·3°	5	3	2
Gold	Au.	‡19·5	2016°	1102·2°	1	1	5
Iron	Fe.	7·8	‡2700°	1482·2°	4	9	1
Lead	Pb.	11·4	612°	322·2°	9	7	8
Nickel	Ni.	8·82	‡2700°	1482·2°	10	10	—
Pewter		Greatly varies with composition.					
Platinum ...	Pt.	21·5	3080°	1693·3°	3	6	3
Silver	Ag.	10·5	1873°	1022·7°	2	2	4
Tin...	Sn.	‡7·3	442°	227·7°	8	4	7
Zinc	Zn.	‡7	773°	411·6°	7	8	6

Further particulars of the characteristics and properties of the metals mentioned in the foregoing table may now be given with advantage, as may also a brief outline of the methods by which the metals are refined or reduced from their ores ; in the case of alloys, the methods of producing them by admixture will be described.

Aluminium. This, the lightest metal that the sheet metal

* Fahrenheit.   † Centigrade.   ‡ Variable.

worker is likely to use, is, when of 98·5 per cent. purity, bright white in colour, somewhat resembling silver, though its appearance depends much on the temperature at which it has been worked. It is capable of taking a high polish. As stated in the table on the previous page, its fusing point is about 1,050° F., but this may be increased to 1,832° F. if impurities are present or if it is alloyed with another metal. Aluminium is only slightly elastic ; it is, however, fairly malleable and ductile, but these latter properties are impaired by the presence of its chief two impurities, silicate and iron. If of more than 99 per cent. purity, it can be rolled, it is said, into leaves 1-40,000th part of an inch in thickness, in this respect being inferior only to gold. Aluminium has a tensile strength of 7 tons to the square inch. When pure, it is non-corrosive and resists the oxidising action of the atmosphere, but this advantage has to be partly sacrificed to obtain increased hardness and elasticity by adding small quantities of copper, nickel, or zinc. It dissolves in hydrochloric acid and in most solutions of the alkalies, but it is only slightly affected by dilute sulphuric acid, and not at all by nitric acid. Rolled or forged metal breaks with a fine silky fracture. Aluminium is not found in a metallic state, but when in combination with oxygen, various alkalies, fluorine, silicon, and acids, it is the base of many clays and soils. Frequent compounds of aluminium are felspar, mica, gneiss, and trachyte, whilst other aluminium compounds, classed as precious stones, are the ruby, sapphire, garnet, turquoise, lazulite, topaz, etc. Those ores from which aluminium is commercially reduced are bauxite, cryolite, and corundum. The chemical method of producing aluminium has been superseded by the cheaper and more satisfactory electrical process. The best known three electrical methods are the Cowles, the Hall, and the Herault, the first-named depending on the heating effect of the electric current and producing aluminium alloys only, whereas by the two latter methods aluminium salts are submitted to electrolytic action at a high temperature, pure metal being produced. The sheet metal worker would do well to thoroughly acquaint himself with the many peculiarities of aluminium, which is replacing other metals for ornamental sheet metal work and in the formation of culinary and other utensils, for which purpose its indifference to the action of most acids and to atmospheric conditions renders it especially suitable. The great disadvantage of aluminium is the difficulty encountered in forming reliable soldered joints in it. This is caused by the formation of an oxide on the surface of the heated metal, the oxide preventing the soft solder from alloying with the aluminium and producing a good joint. With care the difficulty can be surmounted by employing soldering alloys of an easily fusible nature and by melting them with a special copper bit. Good solders for the purpose are given by authorities as follows : (*a*) Tin, 95 parts, and bismuth, 5 parts. (*b*) Tin, 97, bismuth, 3. (*c*) Aluminium, 2·5 ; zinc, 25·25 ; phosphorus, ·25 ; tin, 72. (*d*) Aluminium, 10 ; tin, 90. (*e*) Cadmium, 50 ; zinc, 20 ; tin, 30. The copper bit should be wedge-shape and bent round roughly to a quarter circle ; its edge is then at right angles to the aluminium, and by lightly moving the bit backward and forwards over the metal and the flowing solder the film of oxide can be removed. The coated surface can then be soldered with an ordinary copper bit.

Antimony. This is a bluish white metal, very crystalline and brittle, and so can easily be powdered. Its chief use is in the formation of serviceable alloys, such as Britannia metal, pewter, and Queen's metal, to which it imparts brittleness. The melted metal rapidly oxidizes if exposed to the air, and if highly heated burns with a white flame, giving off fumes of antimony trioxide. Antimony is dissolved by hot hydrochloric acid, hot concentrated sulphuric acid, and aqua regis, and if treated with nitric acid forms a straw-coloured powder known as antimonic acid. Commercial antimony contains impurities in the form of potassium, copper, iron, lead, etc. Antimony occurs native, but generally the metal is found in combination with others ; the chief antimony ore is stibnite. The antimony is recovered from this ore by two distinct processes; by the first of these is separated the antimony sulphide, which is in its turn refined by the second process. In Germany, where much of the commercial antimony comes from, the ore is placed in covered pots having perforated bottoms, below which are receivers. Between the pots is the fire the heat of which fuses the sulphide, which runs through the holes into the receivers. Crucibles heated in circular wind-furnaces are employed to refine the sulphide in England. The charge is 40 lbs. of sulphide and 20 lbs. of scrap-iron, and the product is antimony and iron sulphide, which is again melted, this time with sulphate of soda and some slag, a product of the next process. The resultant metal is melted with pearlash and slag, and cast into ingots. Antimony can be produced by electro-deposition.

Bismuth. This metal is reddish white in colour, and has a bright lustre. It is very brittle and crystalline, volatilises at a high temperature, and, burning, forms a crystalline scale—flowers of bismuth. The, most important use of bismuth is in forming alloys, as its addition to any metal has the effect of considerably lowering the melting-point of that metal. Bismuth may be alloyed with antimony, lead, tin, etc. Bismuth solders may be formed of :—(*a*) Tin, 4 parts ; lead, 4 parts ; bismuth, 1 part. (*b*) Tin, 3 ; lead, 3 ; bismuth, 1. (*c*) Tin, 2 ; lead, 2 ; bismuth, 1. (*d*) Equal parts of tin, lead, and bismuth. (*e*) Tin, 2 ; lead, 1 ; bismuth, 2. (*f*) Tin, 3 ; lead, 5 ; bismuth, 3. Bismuth is found in the metallic state in the form of bismuth-glance (bismuth and sulphur), in combination with oxygen as an ochre, and in the ores of silver, lead, tin, copper, and cobalt. Furnaces for reducing bismuth each contain a number of inclined iron tubes, in which the ore is placed. A wood-fire is lighted, and the fused bismuth, together with some impurities, flows through apertures at the lower ends of the tubes into clay or iron pots heated by a fire underneath. The sulphur and arsenic contained in it are removed by again fusing the metal, this time accompanied by one-tenth its weight of nitre.

Brass. This is a general name for alloys of copper and zinc. Their colour varies with the proportions of the ingredients, though, strictly speaking, the term " brass " can only be applied to those copper and zinc alloys of a decided yellow colour. Ordinary brass is malleable and ductile, especially suitable for casting, and, though harder than copper, melts at a lower temperature than that metal. Unlacquered brass quickly tarnishes under. atmospheric action. By one method of making brass, the zinc and other ingredients are plunged into the molten copper. When the whole is in a molten state, it is stirred with hot brass or iron rods to produce a thorough alloy ; just previous to pouring, some sodium sulphate or sodium carbonate is thrown on to the metal to bring to the surface any impurities, which may then be skimmed. By another method, copper slips are plunged into liquid zinc until an alloy difficult of fusion is formed, when the rest of the copper is added. When cold, the alloy is broken into pieces and melted under charcoal, zinc or copper being added, if necessary, to give the requisite colour and quality. When at a suitable heat, the metal is poured into granite moulds. If the brass is to be made into sheet, it has to undergo a series of annealings and rollings until the desired thinness is attained. Below is given a table of brass alloys, which are but a selection from those that might have been given had space permitted.

Colour or Name of Brass.	Copper.	Zinc.	Tin.	Lead.
Common	1	1	—	—
Good Light	2	1	—	—
Bright Malleable	7	3	—	—
Pinchbeck	4	1	—	—
Tombac	16	1	1	—
Rolled	75	22	3	—
Emerson's Patent	16	8	—	—
Common Pale	25	20	2	3
Fine Pale (brittle)	15	9	4	—
White	1	8	1	—
English	70·29	29·26	0·17	0·28
Ditto	67	32	—	1
French	71·9	25·1	1	2
Red	5	1	—	—
Ditto	72	28	—	—
Sheet-Metal Workers' ...	62	37	1	—
Ditto	83·02	16·98	—	—
Ditto	66·18	38·82	—	—
Ditto	92·7	4·6	2·7	—
Ditto	90	10	—	—
Ditto	83	17	—	—
Ditto	73·5	26·2	0·3	—
Ditto	67	32	0·5	0·5
Ditto	65	35	—	—

Bronze. This is a yellowish, reddish, or chocolate brown alloy of copper and tin, and many of the remarks on brass are applicable to this also. It is made in a similar way, and indeed there does not appear to be a sharp distinction between the two alloys. Bismuth bronze is an alloy of 16 parts of tin, and from 1 to 3 of bismuth. These are the proportions of five of Fontaine Moreau's bronzes : (*a*) Zinc, 90 parts ; copper, 8 ; cast-iron, 1 ; lead, 1. (*b*) Zinc, 92 ; copper, 8. (*c*) Zinc, 92 ; copper, 7 ; cast-iron, 1. (*d*) Zinc, 97 ; copper, 2·5 ; cast-iron, 0·5. (*e*) Zinc, 99 ; copper, 1. For aluminium bronzes, the following proportions have been given : (*a*) Aluminium, 7·5 ; copper, 90 ; gold, 2·5. (*b*) Aluminium, 1 ; copper, 10 ; nickel, 7 ; tungsten, 5. (*c*) Aluminium, 1 ; copper, 10. (*d*) Aluminium, 3 ; copper, 16 ; zinc, 10. Below are given the proportions for some of the better-known bronzes.

COLOUR OR NAME OF BRONZE.	*Copper.*	*Tin.*	*Zinc.*	*Lead.*
Reddish Yellow	51	1	—	—
Ditto	16	1	—	—
Ditto	13	1	—	—
Yellow Red	8	1	—	—
Ditto	16	2·5	—	—
Bluish Red	16	3	—	—
Ditto	16	3·5	—	—
Ash Grey	4	1	—	—
Dark Grey	16	5	—	—
Whitish	16	7	—	—
Ditto (better)	16	8	—	—
Ditto (best)	8	16	—	—
Statuary	88	9	2	1
Ditto	91	9	—	—
Ditto	91	2	5·5	—
Very Hard	50	7	—	—
Antique	87	13	—	—
Ditto	97	3	—	—

Copper. This is a well-known, highly malleable, ductile, and tenacious red metal greatly used in many industrial arts, and especially by the sheet metal worker. It does not resist the action of acids, and even moisture affects it, causing it to form an oxide known as verdigris ; this, under the action of carbonic acid, turns to a green carbonate. Copper is also caused to oxidize by heat ; it is volatile only at a great heat. Commercial copper contains many impurities, amongst them being iron, silver, bismuth, antimony, arsenic, lead, tin, sulphur, and many others. Copper is much used in its commercially pure state, but is greatly in demand as the chief ingredient of the important brass and bronze alloys. Copper sometimes occurs native, being then often covered with an oxide and carbonate crust; it is sometimes found in grains in sand, but is more generally obtained by the reduction of its ores, which are very plentiful. The ores may be reduced—

(1) by treating them in reverberatory or blast furnaces, or in both ; (2) by the " wet " method ; or (3) by the electro-chemical method. Limited space will not allow descriptions of all these methods, so brief outlines of two of the furnace methods and the "wet" method will have to suffice. By one German process the ore is oxidized and the sulphur expelled by roasting, and the ore is then smelted in a cupola, two cisterns receiving respectively the slag and metal which flow through tap-holes. Repeated roasting is necessary, and then all sulphates are removed by lixiviation. Silver is removed with lead, which is afterwards separated by cupellation. By another method the copper pyrites is roasted together with chloride of sodium, thus causing sulphuric acid to be formed ; this attacks the soda, and the copper is converted to a soluble sulphate, the iron of the pyrites being then in the form of peroxide. The fumes of the chlorine, set free from the sodium chloride, impregnate lime, and this becomes a bleaching agent. The wet method of treating copper is to grind and roast it, mix it with salt, and again roast it so as to form copper chloride and sodium sulphate, which are then dissolved in dilute acids. Any silver which may be in solution is precipitated by the action of zinc iodide, and the copper chloride solution is siphoned off and precipitated with scrap-iron. After washing the precipitate, it is refined in reverberatory furnaces. The copper from these may be cast into slabs, and to make these into thin sheets the slabs are annealed and rolled repeatedly, the rolls being brought nearer to each other at each successive operation ; the copper is annealed after each rolling.

Gold. This yellow and lustrous metal has a very limited application in the art of the sheet metal worker, but merely, be it said, on account of its comparative scarcity to other metals, and hence its expensiveness. Were it not for this, its high malleability and ductility would cause it to be very extensively used in many of the industrial arts. So malleable is gold that it may be reduced to leaves only the 290,000th part of an inch in thickness. It is but very slightly affected by the atmosphere, and resists the action of all solvents with the exception of selenic, aqua regia, and aqueous chlorine. Gold is found in a metallic state in the form of grains in sand, etc., and it is then often in combination with silver, copper, platinum, iron, etc. Veins of gold quartz occur, and occasionally the metal is found native in lumps, termed nuggets. The ores of galena, copper pyrites, iron, etc., sometimes contain traces of gold. There are many methods of extracting gold from the ores—the chemical, electro-chemical, etc.—but as the use of the metal is so restricted in the sheet metal worker's craft, no useful purpose would be served by mentioning the methods of extraction here.

Iron. As a pure metal, iron is practically unknown in sheet-metal working, though steel, which is mere iron containing from 0·15 to 1·8 of carbon, has a very wide application in the form of tin-plate, more correctly termed tinned plate. There is no need to give here particulars of the many processes attendant on the production of iron or steel, the information given under the heading of Tinned Steel being quite sufficient for the purpose of the metal plate worker.

Lead. This metal is of a bluish-grey colour, and is lustrous when freshly cut. Being very malleable, ductile, and tough, it is greatly used in most of the crafts. It has but little elasticity. It is very soft, and can be cold-welded by pressure. Lead is not affected by most acids, but moisture and nitric acid rapidly oxidise it. As stated in the table on p. 10, its melting-point is 612° F.; and if it is slowly cooled from this temperature, it crystallises into octohedrons. Lead is largely worked in the form of sheet, but not by the sheet metal worker, whose use for lead is limited. Sheet-lead is of two kinds, cast and rolled, the latter being known as milled, and it is jointed when occasion requires in one of two ways, soldering or burning. Lead is easily fused, and enters into the composition of many useful alloys, some of which are solders. Lead occurs in the form of ore, and generally as sulphide of lead, known commercially as galena. This has a metallic lustre, and often is in crystallised cubes, always containing silver. Less important lead ores are cerusite, a dirty white substance containing, besides lead, carbon and oxygen; pyromorphite, a green, yellow, or brown ore containing, besides lead, phosphorus, carbon, oxygen, and chlorine; mimetesite, which is similar to pyro-morphite, but contains arsenic in the place of phosphorus; and anglesite, a white or grey ore composed of lead, sulphur, and oxygen. In the reduction of the principal ore—galena—it is first picked, then broken and washed, and then a portion of it roasted and mixed with the unroasted portion. The whole is then roasted to remove the sulphur.

Nickel. This is a white, malleable, ductile, and tenacious metal capable of receiving a silver polish. It resembles iron in

B

some respects, being magnetic, weldable, and being influenced by carbon, which has the effect of lowering its melting point ; the latter in pure nickel is but a little below that of iron. Nickel is not readily oxidized by an ordinary atmosphere, but oxidation takes place when heated. It is but little affected by most acids, but is easily dissolved by nitric acid. Nickel has its most useful application in the formation of alloys, the chief of these being German silver or nickel silver, consisting of zinc, copper, and nickel in varying proportions ; sometimes iron enters into the composition. Some popular formulæ for German or nickel silvers are these : (*a*) Copper, 40·4 parts ; iron, 2·6 parts ; zinc, 25·4 parts ; nickel, 31·6 parts. (*b*) Copper, 67 ; zinc, 13·6 ; nickel, 19·3. (*c*) Copper, 62·4 ; zinc, 22·15 ; nickel, 15·45. (*d*) Copper, 62·6 ; zinc, 26·55 ; nickel, 10·85. The principal nickel ores are : Smaltine or smaltite, from which smalts, zaffre, and cobalt are obtained ; this after calcination yields nickel speise, a yellowish white and brittle combination of nickel, arsenic, sulphur, iron, etc. ; Kupfer nickel (copper nickel) which is copper-coloured and has a metallic lustre ; nickel pyrites, which is a brassy-looking ore ; millerite (hair pyrites) and pyrrholite (magnetic pyrites), which are sulphides of nickel ; garnierite, which is a hydrous silicate of iron, magnesia, etc., and is of an apple-green colour. The wet method of extracting the nickel from the ore, as largely adopted, is as follows :—Arsenic and sulphur are removed by calcination from the ground ore, which is then made into a solution with hot hydrochloric acid to which bleaching powder is then added so as to peroxidize the iron, which falls to the bottom in the form of basic arseniate of iron. Sulphide of copper is precipitated by treatment with sulphuretted hydrogen, which is then boiled out of the filtrate. Bleaching powder is added to the precipitate oxide of cobalt, the solution is filtered, and then boiled with milk of lime (an emulsion of calcium hydrate) to precipitate nickel oxide, which is then reduced by making it into a paste with carbon, cutting it into cakes or cubes, and heating these, surrounded with charcoal, in crucibles or tubes to a white heat.

Pewter. This is a greyish-silvery alloy of tin and lead, though other metals may be added or may take the place of the lead. A greater quantity than 20 per cent. lead makes the alloy of a bluish colour. The alloy is hardened by the addition of antimony. Whilst the metals are being melted together the contents of the crucible are stirred with a strip of tin and zinc alloy, or a lump of zinc is placed on the surface of the melted metal. This "cleanses" the alloy, that is, prevents the formation of dross. The table below gives the proportions and ingredients of the principal pewter alloys.

NAME OR CLASS OF PEWTER.	Tin.	Lead.	Anti-mony.	Copper.	Zinc.	Bis-muth.
Ordinary	82	18	—	—	—	—
Better	84	—	7	4	—	—
Ditto	89	—	7	2	—	2
Ditto	56	8	—	6	2	—
Superior	50	—	8·5	—	—	—
Hard	48	—	4	1	—	—
Plate	50	—	4	2	—	2
Ditto	90	—	7	2	—	2
Trifle	83	—	17	—	—	—
Ley	80	20	—	—	—	—
Aiken's	50	—	4	2	—	—

Pewter has not a very wide application in sheet-metal working, as that term is usually understood. Pewter is chiefly worked by hammering, or the metal is melted and cast into moulds, the article being afterwards finished in the lathe if its shape admits of such treatment.

Platinum. This is a brilliantly white metal, soft, malleable, ductile, tenacious, and capable of being easily welded. It is fused only by a compound blowpipe flame, an oxy-hydrogen flame, or by the electric arc. It resists the action of moisture or single acids ; aqua regia dissolves platinum, but not readily. It is a very heavy metal, having a specific gravity of 21·5. Platinum lends itself well to the methods of the worker in sheet metal, but its high cost forbids its extensive use in that direction. It is largely employed as an ingredient of many important alloys. Platinum occurs native, and also in combination with iridium, rhodium, palladium, gold, copper, iron, osmium, lead, etc. It is recovered from the ore by one of two methods. In the one case, after the ore has been washed, the gold and silver are separated by amalgamation, and the residue is treated with nitric acid so as to dissolve away the base metals—iron, copper, etc. A solution of platinum chloride is then formed by boiling with aqua regia, the acid being afterwards evaporated. It is then dissolved in water and mixed with alcohol, and a solution of ammonium is employed to precipitate the platinum in the form of a double chloride. The chloride is washed and dried, and then burnt in a plumbago crucible, in which the platinum is left as a black powder, which requires to be welded by the aid of heat and pressure to become compact. By the dry method of Deville and Debray the ore is treated in a reverberatory furnace with galena or litharge, the resultant alloy of lead and platinum being subsequently expelled. An ordinary furnace is unsuitable for the finishing stages of this latter process on account of the great heat required to fuse platinum, so an oxy-hydrogen furnace having a lime hearth is employed. Such a furnace is also used to refine the spongy metal produced by the former method.

Silver. Of this lustrous white metal much can be said that was said of gold. Its many desirable properties—malleability, ductility, tenacity, softness, etc.—make it especially suitable for manipulation by the methods of the sheet metal worker, but its cost forbids its general employment. It does not oxidise under atmospheric influences, but when in a molten state absorbs oxygen, "spitting" it out again on cooling. Although inaccessible on account of its cost as a sheet metal for everyday employment, it enters into the formation of several well-known alloys, and is a valuable constituent of many solders. Silver occurs in a native state and in sulphides, chlorides, bromides, and iodides, and, together with lead, zinc, copper, and iron, in ores. The ores are reduced by one of two systems, wet or dry, and each of these comprises two or three different methods.

Tin. This metal has nearly the lustrous whiteness of silver, is highly malleable, harder than lead, but is not very tenacious. It oxidises only on being heated, when it forms stannic oxide. Tin can be decomposed by many acids, and, as has already been shown, easily alloys with most metals. Tin-plate as used by the sheet metal worker is not solid tin, but steel-plate thinly coated with tin by a process which is described under the heading of Tinned Steel. Many of the more important alloys have tin as their principal constituent ; some of these alloys are solders. Tin occurs in the form of sulphuret and oxide, but more generally in the form of ore, known as tin-stone. This is smelted either in blast or reverberatory furnaces. In the latter case the treatment is in two stages, one being the actual extraction of the metal and the other the refining. The roasted ore is washed to remove the sulphates, and is then placed in a furnace having an inclined bed and lined with about 8 inches of fireclay. Previous to placing in the furnace, the ore is mixed with anthracite and a small quantity of lime and fluor-spar. At the end of five hours more anthracite is thrown into the furnace, and in about an hour after that the molten metal can be run off. The remaining slag is an iron silicate which contains some oxides. To refine the pig-tin, it is placed in a reverberatory furnace and gradually heated to about 450° Fahrenheit ; at this temperature the tin melts, and is drawn off into iron pots. The mass left in the furnace is "hard head," and contains for the most part iron. On again melting the tin and stirring it with a pole of green wood, it is caused to boil by the escape of gases, and by this means the impurities, such as iron and arsenic, are brought to the surface, from which they are skimmed. Grain tin is made by allowing the molten metal to fall from a height on to a hard cold surface. To produce what is known as "common" tin, the metal passes at once to the granite moulds. "Refined" tin is the result of using better ores and lengthening the poling process. The purest metal in the mould is the upper portion ; the middle portion is the "common," and the bottom portion is too impure for use at all, and requires another fusing and poling. The ingots are known as "block" tin.

Tinned Steel. The material with which the sheet metal worker has most to do, and with which he should be most conversant, is sheet-steel coated with tin, and known in the trade as tin-plate. Before giving particulars of the sizes in which these plates are sold, their weights and other particulars, it is as well to fully describe the methods by which the tinned plates are produced.

Tin-plate is almost entirely made from steel manufactured either by the Bessemer process or in open-hearth furnaces, and, though the chemical composition of the metal from either process is almost identical, the latter is considered superior. Before these methods came into vogue, the highest quality of tin-bar made was termed "charcoal plate," while the second quality was called "coke plate," these names signifying the mode of manufacture of the iron used. These terms are still retained to indicate the quality, plate produced from open-hearth steel being called charcoal plate, and that from Bessemer steel being called coke plate, though now the names do not refer to the mode of production.

The ingots of steel, whether open-hearth or Bessemer, if the tests as to the quality have been satisfactory, are passed on to the re-heating furnace preparatory to rolling. When properly heated the ingots are rolled into "tin bars" about 7 in. wide, varying in thickness from $\frac{3}{8}$ in. to $\frac{5}{8}$ in., according to the size of plates to be produced from them.

The chemical composition of tin bar should be as follows, per cent.: ·09 to ·11 of carbon, not more than ·01 of silicon, ·04 to ·07 of sulphur, ·04 to ·06 of phosphorus, ·40 to ·50 of manganese, not less than 99·25 of iron.

The bars are sheared off into $1\frac{1}{2}$-ft. to 2-ft. lengths, which are placed in packs on the coke bottom of a slow draught re-heating furnace and heated to dull red ; after this they are rolled, in the direction of their width, five or more times between chilled rolls, re-heated again and rolled twice, across the original fibre, to a length of about $5\frac{1}{2}$ ft., then doubled, re-heated, and rolled about three times through a second pair of rolls, more carefully turned, to give them a very smooth surface, till each is drawn out to a length of about 5 ft., being then two plates 5 feet long united at one end. These combined plates, while still hot, are again doubled, re-heated, and rolled twice, till they are extended to about 43 in., the whole forming four plates.

The operation of doubling and re-heating is repeated, and the plates are rolled in "eights" twice, until they are stretched out to the required length and thickness. Sometimes the doubling and re-heating are once more repeated, the plates being rolled in "sixteens." The re-heating furnaces are designed and worked in such a manner that the heating of the bars and sheets may proceed gradually and regularly ; the heat must not be so high as to weld the sheets together or cause excessive scaling, and the bars and sheets must be separated frequently. The scale formed between the doubled sheets through excessive heat or too keen a draught will subsequently be rolled into the steel, causing rough surfaces, and consequently defective plates.

After the rolling, the plates are sheared to size ; the "eight" or "sixteen" plates adhere tightly together, and are separated by first bending up one corner, opening them out by means of a small hatchet, and tearing apart by hand. The defective plates are carefully sorted out, and the "black plate," as it is now called, is passed on for pickling, to clean the surfaces.

The "pickling" consists of subjecting the plates to the action of heated dilute sulphuric acid to remove the scale. For the first pickle, about 6 lb. or 7 lb. of sulphuric acid is used per hundred-weight of black plate. In small works the pickling is done in lead-lined tanks by hand, but larger establishments employ machinery for the purpose of more rapidly exposing the surface to the acid, and then washing the acid away when the pickling is complete. The acid leaves the plate with a clean, dullish-grey metallic surface. Sometimes the action of the acid is assisted by scouring with sand and water. When no mechanical apparatus is used the plates are immersed in the acid bath for from fifteen to twenty minutes.

The cleaned plates, free from scale, are now ready for the first annealing process. The effect of the repeated rolling is to make the plates very stiff and brittle, and this has to be remedied by subjecting them to a long-continued heat and allowing them to cool slowly ; this process is called annealing. The plates are piled one upon another on a cast-iron base plate, and covered over with a hood or cover to protect them from oxidation. The edges of the base plate stand higher than the rest, so that, when the cover is placed over the pile of plates, the space between the cover and the edge of the bottom plate may be luted with sand. The boxes are conveyed to the furnace by means of a low bogie supported on wheels.

The annealing furnace has its bed on a level with the floor, several boxes being placed in it at one time. The fire-bridge is tolerably high, and the flame travels slowly over the boxes, gradually raising them to a cherry-red heat, at which temperature they are maintained for from twelve to twenty-four hours, the heat never being allowed to become so great as to cause the plates to become stuck together, or it will be impossible to separate them when the piles are removed from the boxes after cooling.

The plates are then cold-rolled between chilled rolls which have a highly polished surface and are very accurately adjusted, so that the plates may be perfectly flat and the surface finely polished. A second annealing is now necessary to remove the stiffening effect of the cold-rolling, but the temperature of the furnace is kept lower and the time is shortened to about six hours.

After having been annealed and cold-rolled, the plates are again found to be thinly coated with oxide, which must be entirely removed by a second pickling in acid, though the strength of the acid solution is very much weaker, being only

1 lb. of acid to the hundredweight of plates. Scouring with sand and water is then generally resorted to, after which the plates are placed in troughs of clean running water. They should now have a perfectly clean surface of a greyish metallic colour, and can be kept in cold water without injury for some time. In all the stages so far described any defective plates are carefully sorted out, but in spite of this it is sometimes found that during the process of tinning some of the plates are covered with small blisters, due to some defect in the steel.

Coating the plates with tin is the next and last operation. Cast-iron pots, some containing tin and some grease, are arranged in a row and surrounded by a flue from a fireplace. The black plates are taken up singly from the water, and placed in the first pot containing molten palm-oil until all moisture has been removed. They are then transferred to a pot containing molten tin covered with palm-oil.

After remaining a short time the plates are lifted out, and, to make the alloy of tin on the surface more perfect, they are dipped into the second tin pot containing pure molten tin. The excess of tin is brushed off each side of the sheet by means of a hempen brush, and the marks of the brush are obliterated by again dipping the sheets into pure tin in the third tin pot. The operation of tinning is completed by quickly passing each sheet from the third tin pot into the second grease pot, which contains an arrangement of rollers between which the tin-plates pass, first downwards, then upwards and out. The temperature of the second grease pot is carefully regulated, for its object is to allow the excess of tin to run off the surface of the plates ; the speed of the rolls and the pressure regulate the quantity of tin left on the finished plate. Coke plates take up about $2\frac{1}{2}$ lb. of tin to the hundredweight, being passed slowly through the rollers in the grease pot under considerable pressure ; while charcoal plates have a thicker coating of about 6 lb. of tin per hundredweight, as they are passed twice quickly through the rolls, which are adjusted to give less pressure.

To remove the grease left on the plates from the last stage of the tinning process, they are rubbed with coarse bran and then with finer bran, being finally polished with a duster made of the woolly side of a sheepskin.

It only remains now to carefully sort the plates and pack them in boxes with sheets of paper between. There are about forty-five different descriptions of tin-plate manufactured; they are divided into nine varieties of dimensions, advancing from 14 in. × 10 in. to 34 in. × 25 in., and they are contained in boxes weighing from 94 lb. to 257 lb. each, in fifteen different stages. The number of sheets in each box varies from twenty-five up to 225 in the nine different dimensions.

Tinned plates measuring 14 in. × 10 in. are known as singles; 15 in. × 11 in., middles or small doubles; 17 in. × 12½ in., doubles; 20 in. × 14 in., large doubles or twenties. The other sizes are generally called by their dimensions, such as 28 in. × 20 in., 30 in. × 22 in., 40 in. × 20 in., and various other sizes. The thickness of these plates is denoted by the number of crosses on the box; thus there are one cross single, two cross double, and so on; it is written thus: 1 × s, one cross single; 1 × × s, two cross single; the 1 is always prefixed, no matter how many crosses there are; thus, 1 × × × × D is 4 cross double, and is a 4 × plate 17 in. × 12½ in.; the word double has no relation whatever to thickness. The following short table shows the weights of tinned plate of various thicknesses, as compared with the weights of sheet copper, brass, and zinc.

Thickness in Inches.	B.W.G.	Strength of Tinned Steel (Approximate).	Weight in lbs. per sq. ft.			
			Tinned Steel.	Copper.	Brass.	Zinc.
·012	30	1C	·48	·55	·52	·42
·014	28	1×	·56	·69	·65	·56
·016	27	DC	·64	·83	·79	·62
·018	26	1× ×	·72	·92	·87	
·020	25	1× × × ×	·80	·97	·92	·71
·025	23	D× × ×	1·0	1·29	1·22	·93
·028	22	D× × × ×	1·13	1·34	1·27	1·06
·032	21	D× × × × ×	1·29	1·52	1·44	1·12

Zinc. This bluish-white and highly crystalline metal is very malleable when pure, but impure commercial zinc is inclined to be brittle. Cast zinc is named spelter, only the rolled metal being known as zinc. Zinc oxidises at a red heat, but the rolled metal forms a film of grey suboxide at an ordinary temperature if in a damp situation. Zinc is hardened by rolling, and is annealed at a low heat to again make it malleable Pure zinc is dissolved by nitric acid and alkalis, but not by hydrochloric or sulphuric acid, though commercial zinc is readily dissolved by either of these acids. Zinc is much used as a pure metal, and also in alloys. "Galvanised iron" is sheet-steel coated with zinc. Methods of galvanising metals are described fully on pp. 112–114. The chief ores of zinc are zincite (red oxide of zinc), a white ore when pure, but is usually of a reddish colour owing to the presence of oxide of manganese ; blende or "black jack," a sulphide which is a black or yellowish-black ore, with sometimes a reddish tinge imparted by galena ; calamine, a carbonate ; and electric calamine, a silicate. Zinc is very volatile, and thus has to be extracted from its ores by distillation. In reducing blende, it is first oxidised and then treated with carbon and carbonic oxide, or by hydrogen and hydrocarbons. The powdered blende is roasted in a reverberatory furnace until most of the sulphur has disappeared, and the zinc oxide remaining is heated in fire-clay retorts to a temperature of about 1,000° C. (1,832° F.), when the vapours are condensed.

CHAPTER II.

GEOMETRICAL CONSTRUCTION OF PLANE FIGURES.

Now that the reader is in possession of information concerning the properties and characteristics of the materials which are shaped by the art of the metal plate worker, it is necessary that he should become acquainted with the methods of drawing or, as it is termed, "setting out" patterns. Of course, it is impossible to describe the individual development of every article constructed of sheet metal, but each and all of the geometrical exercises involved in producing any pattern will be fully explained.

Drawing for metal plate work consists in applying geometry to the development of surfaces. A knowledge of a few elementary geometric constructions is necessary, as, by the application of these, most of the regular plane figures may be drawn.

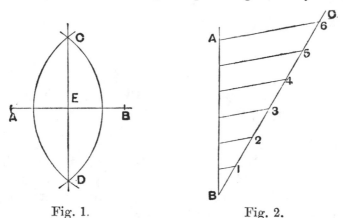

Fig. 1.   Fig. 2.

Fig. 1.—Line divided into Two Equal Parts ; Fig. 2.—Line divided into a number of Equal Parts.

These elementary problems frequently recur, and they should be committed to memory, together with the complete plane figures throughout the work.

To divide a line into two equal parts. PROBLEM 1.—Let A B (Fig. 1) be the given line. With the points A B on the given line as centres, and with any radius greater than half the length of the line, describe arcs intersecting at c and d. Join c and d by a line that cuts A B at e, the centre of the line.

To divide a given straight line into any required number of equal parts. PROBLEM 2.—Let A B (Fig. 2) be the given line, and from one end set off a line, as B C, at any suitable angle, and, with the dividers, step off along B C a number of equal divisions, 1, 2, 3, etc., corresponding to the number of divisions required in A B, in this case six. Join the last division point 6 to A, and draw lines parallel to 6 A through 1, 2, 3, etc., to cut A B. These lines will divide A B into the required number of equal parts.

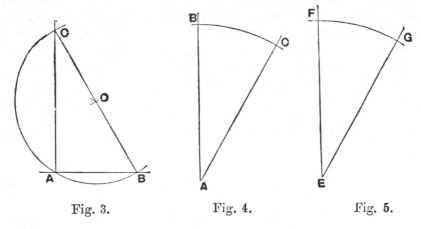

Fig. 3.   Fig. 4.   Fig. 5.

Fig. 3.—Line drawn perpendicular to Given Line; Figs. 4 and 5.— Drawing Angle equal to Given Angle.

To draw a straight line perpendicular to a given straight line at a given point. PROBLEM 3.—Let A B (Fig. 3) be the given line, and A the given point. With any suitable length (as A B) as radius and using A and B as centres, describe arcs intersecting at o. Using o as centre, and with radius o A or o B, describe an arc. Join B o, and produce the line to intersect the arc at c. Then join A to c.

To draw an angle equal to a given angle. PROBLEM 4.— Let B A C (Fig. 4) be the given angle. With the angular point A as centre and any suitable length as radius, describe an arc B C. With the same radius, and with any point (E, Fig. 5) along a straight line E F as centre, describe an arc F G. Take the distance B C (Fig. 4) as radius, and with F (Fig. 5) as centre, cut the arc at G. Join G to E to make the required angle. This problem is useful in setting out a given throat angle for an elbow.

To bisect an angle. PROBLEM 5.—Let B A C (Fig. 6) be the given angle. Using A as centre, and with any convenient radius, describe an arc B C. With centres at B and C, and with a radius greater than half the distance between B and C, describe arcs intersecting at D. A line drawn from D to A will divide the angle as required.

To bisect an angle contained between two lines when the point at which the lines would meet is inaccessible. PROBLEM 6.—The angle is contained between the lines A B, Fig. 7. At any part of each line erect equal perpendiculars, as C E and D F, and from their extremities draw lines parallel to A and B, intersecting in G. Bisect the angle E G F (as in Problem 5), and the line G H will bisect the angle contained between the lines A and B.

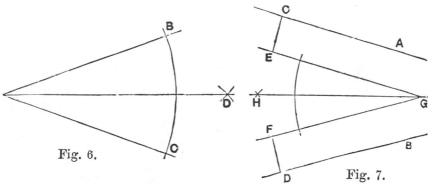

Fig. 6.—Bisected Angle; Fig. 7.—Bisecting Angle having Inaccessible Vertex.

To draw a circle or an arc of a circle to pass through any three given points. PROBLEM 7.—Let A B C (Fig. 8) be the given points. With any suitable length as radius, and A and B as centres, describe arcs intersecting at D and E. Again use any suitable length as radius, and with B and C as centres, describe arcs intersecting at D^1 and E^1. Draw straight lines through D E and $D^1 E^1$ to meet at the point O. Use O as centre and radius to A, B, or C to draw the required circle or arc. This construction could also be used for finding the centre of any given circle. Mark any three points on the circumference of the given circle, and then proceed as above.

To draw an arc when centre of circle is inaccessible. PROBLEM 8.—Let A B (Fig. 9) be the chord of the arc and D C its rise. From A and B as centres, with the radius A B,

describe the arcs A E and B F.   From A draw a line through
C, cutting the arc B F in G.   From B draw a line through C,
cutting the arc A E in H.   Divide A H and B G into any
number of equal parts, as 1, 2, 3, 4, 5, and set off a number of

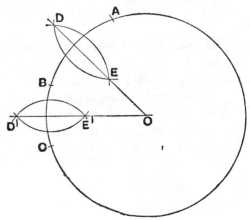

Fig. 8.—Circle to pass through Three Given Points.

these parts from G to F and H to E, as i, ii, iii, iv, v.   Draw lines
from A to 1, 2, 3, 4, 5, and from B to i, ii, iii, iv, v.   Then it will
be seen that the first line above H, namely to i, intersects the
first line below G, namely to 1, in the point X.   Again, the line

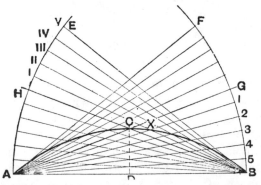

Fig. 9.—Drawing Portion of Circle when centre is inaccessible.

to 2 will intersect that to ii, line 3 will intersect iii, and lines
4 and 5 will cut iv and v.   Proceed in the same manner on
the opposite side, and through the intersections trace the curve
by hand.

For inking, a templet may be made, and as this plan will be
recommended in several other cases, the mode of making this

useful article is given. Draw the figure accurately on a smooth piece of veneer ; if of a light colour so much the better, or a small quantity of veneer may have a sheet of thin white paper glued over it.   Cut out the form near the curve required, and bring it exactly up to shape by means of a fine file—a half-round one is best for this, as with it both concave and convex surfaces can be finished.   The final smoothing is then to be done with fine glass-paper, and in this process the edges should be very slightly bevelled off, in order to prevent the ink dragging on the paper. Sets of curves of different radii, and "French curves" of various forms, may be purchased, and will be found very useful for this purpose.

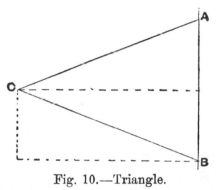

Fig. 10.—Triangle.

To draw any given triangle. PROBLEM 9.—A triangle is a figure formed by three straight lines. To draw a triangle, as in Fig. 10, mark the length of one side upon a straight line A B. With the length of a second side as radius, and taking as centre the corresponding angular point A, describe an arc. With the length of the third side as radius and B as centre, draw a second arc to intersect the first in c.   Then join A to c and B to c.

To draw a square of given side. PROBLEM 10.—A square is a figure having four equal sides, and all its angles right angles. On the given side A B (Fig. 11) erect a perpendicular at A (Problem 3), and with A as centre, A B as radius, cut A c in c. Then with the same radius, and centres B and c, describe arcs that intersect in D. Join c to D and B to D to complete the square.

To draw a rectangle of given sides. PROBLEM 11.—A rectangle has its opposite sides equal, and all its angles right angles. Draw the two sides at right angles as A B and A c in Fig. 12.   Then with c as centre, and radius A B, describe an arc ; and with B as centre, and radius A C, describe another arc to intersect the first at D. Join c D and B D, and the rectangle will be complete.

To divide a circle into any number of equal parts. PROBLEM 12. —A circle is a plane figure contained by one curved line, called the circumference, and is such that all points on the circumference are equally distant from a point within the circle, called the centre. A diameter is a straight line drawn through the centre and terminated at both ends by the circumference. A radius is a straight line drawn from the centre to the circumference. An arc is a portion of the circumference, and a chord is the straight line joining the ends of an arc.

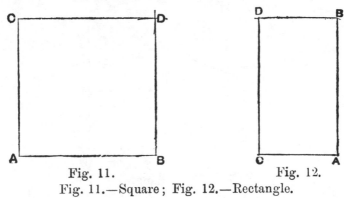

Fig. 11.   Fig. 12.
Fig. 11.—Square; Fig. 12.—Rectangle.

The following constructions, which require the compasses only, are best made with the steel dividers, and if two or three pairs can be employed, some distances (such as the radius of the circle) often required can be kept unaltered. With the given radius describe the circle (Fig. 13), and, with the same radius in the compass, step round the circle, thus dividing it into six equal parts in B, C, D, E, F, and G. B E is a diameter, and therefore divides it into two equal parts. A line drawn from B to D would be a chord of two-sixths or one-third ; the circle is divided in B, D, and F into three equal parts.

From B with D as radius, and from E with C as radius, describe arcs intersecting in X both above and below the diameter B E. Then a line being drawn through the points X X, the circumference will be divided into four equal parts H, B, I, and E. A is the centre of the circle.

The arcs described with the radius A B with X X as centres will cut the circumference in K, L, M, and N, which points bisect the quadrants B H, H E, E I, and I B, and thus divide the circle into eight equal parts.

The radius A B, set off from H I to O P Q R, bisects the arcs B C, D E, E F, and G B, which completes the trisection of each quadrant, and therefore divides the circle into twelve equal parts.

The radius A B, set off both ways around the circumference from K, L, M, and N, will respectively give the points S, Y, V, U, T, W, Z, and J, and thus complete the division of the circle into twenty-four equal parts. Any further subdivision may be done

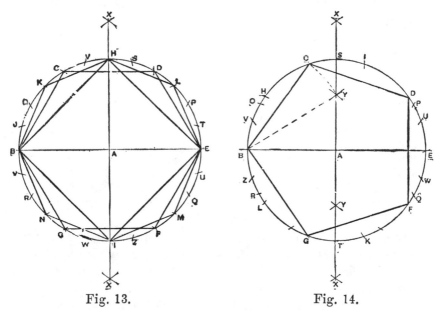

Fig. 13.   Fig. 14.

Figs. 13 and 14.—Circles divided into Number of Equal Parts.

either by bisecting the arcs already formed, or by trial. Thus it is obvious that if each of the twenty-four parts is bisected, the circle will be divided into forty-eight parts.

The foregoing constructions are performed, it will be seen, by three distances only—the radius A B, the chord D B, and A X——consequently, if these be kept unaltered in separate pairs of dividers, the operations are performed with the greatest accuracy.

In order to avoid confusion, the continuation of this problem is given separately in Fig. 14. With the distance A X as radius, describe arcs respectively from O and P, and from Q and R; these arcs will intersect at Y Y. Then the distance B Y or E Y, stepped

C

around the circumference, will divide it into five equal parts in B, C, D, F, and G ; the distance A Y will bisect the arcs B C, C D, D F, etc., in H, I, E, K, and L, and thus divide the circle into ten parts.

The distance B Y set off from S and T (the extremities of the diameter perpendicular to B E) will bisect the arcs D E, B H, E F, and B L, in the points U, V, W, and Z, and will thus give one-twentieth of the circumference. The same distance being set off from these points will bisect the other arcs of the decagon. The division into forty parts may be effected by bisecting the arcs last found. These methods, when once clearly understood, are extremely useful in the rapid construction of regular polygons. Of course, no more of the figure need be worked than is necessary for the immediate purpose.

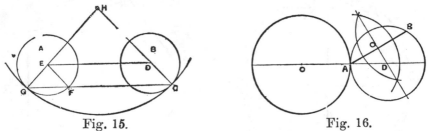

Fig. 15.   Fig. 16.

Fig. 15. – Circle touching two Given Circles ; Fig. 16.—Circle touching another Circle at Given Point.

To describe a circle touching two given circles, and one of them at a given point of contact. PROBLEM 13.—A and B (Fig. 15) are the two circles, and C is the required point of contact. Join the centres D and E. Draw a line from C passing through D, and produce it. At E draw E F parallel to D C. Draw C F parallel to E D, and produce it to G. Draw G E and produce it until it intersects C D produced in H. From H, with radius H C, describe the required circle, a portion of which is shown.

To draw a circle touching another circle in a given point, and passing through a given point lying without the circle. PROBLEM 14. —Let A (Fig. 16) be the point of contact in the given circle, and B the point lying without it. The centre of the required circle will evidently lie on the radius O A produced, and on a perpendicular at the middle of a line joining A B, which line will be a chord of the required circle. Therefore, produce O A, draw a line from A to B, and bisect it in C. Produce the bisecting line until it cuts O A produced in D, which is the centre of the required circle, D A being the radius

To join by an arc of a circle two lines inclined to each other.
PROBLEM 15.—Let A F and B D (Fig. 17) be the two lines. Produce
both until they meet in C. Bisect the angle A C B. At D, the
extremity of one of the lines, erect a perpendicular cutting the
bisector in E. From E, with radius E D, describe the arc which

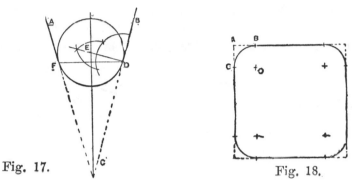

Fig. 17.

Fig. 18.

Fig. 17.—Two Lines inclined to each other by Arc of Circle;
Fig. 18.—Square with Rounded Corners.

will meet the other line in F. If the point C is not accessible, the
angle must be bisected by the method shown in Problem 6, p. 29.

To draw a rectangle or square with rounded corners. PROBLEM
16.—First draw the complete square or rectangle as in Fig. 18,
and then mark off from the corners as at A an equal length along

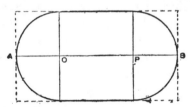

Fig. 19.—Figure with Parallel Sides and Semicircular Ends.

the side and end of the figure at B and C. Use the same length
as radius, and with centres B and C describe arcs intersecting at
O. Use O as centre, and draw the quadrant required from B to C.

To draw a figure with parallel sides and semicircular ends.
PROBLEM 17.—Mark the length of the figure along a straight line
as A B (Fig. 19), and on this line from A and B mark off half the
width of the required figure as O and P; draw lines at right
angles to A B through O and P. Using O and P as centres, and
with radius equal to O A, describe a semicircle on each end of the
figure, and then join the ends of the semicircles by straight lines.

To draw a regular polygon when the length of one side is given. PROBLEM 18.—All figures with more than four sides are called polygons ; when all the sides and angles are equal the figure is said to be a regular polygon. Of such figures, that with five sides is called a pentagon ; six sides, hexagon ; seven sides, heptagon; eight sides, octagon ; nine sides, nonagon ; ten sides, decagon ; and twelve sides, duodecagon. Let A B (Fig. 20) be the given side. With B as centre, and A B as radius, describe a

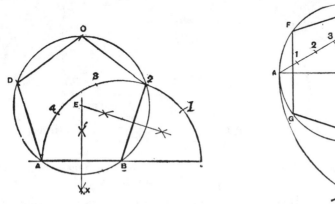

Fig. 20.   Fig. 21.

Fig. 20.—Polygon ; Fig. 21.—Polygon inscribed within Circle.

semicircle, and divide the semicircle into equal parts by trial with dividers, corresponding in number to the number of sides the polygon is to have—in this case, five. Through the second division point 2 draw a line to join B. Bisect A B and B 2. Produce the lines of bisection until they intersect at E. Using E as centre, and with radius to E A or E B, describe a circle, and on the circumference mark off by the compasses the remaining division points D C ; join A D, D C, C 2 by straight lines to complete the figure.

To inscribe a polygon within a circle of given size. PROBLEM 19. —Draw a circle to the given size, and draw the diameter A B (Fig. 21). From A at any angle set off A C, and on it mark off equal divisions corresponding in number to the number of sides the figure is to have—in this case, five ; join the last division point 5 to B, and draw a second line parallel to 5 B through 3 to J on the line A B. With A B as radius, and A and B as alternate centres, describe arcs intersecting at D. Draw through D J a line, and produce it to cut the circle at E ; join

E to B. Then, using this length as radius, mark off the remaining divisions B H, H G, G F, and F E. Join these points by straight lines to complete the figure. A simple, but not a time-saving method would be to step round the circle with the compasses, thus dividing the circle into equal parts, corresponding in number to the number of sides required on the polygon.

To describe a regular polygon about a given circle. PROBLEM 20.—The required polygon is in this case a hexagon. Divide the circle (Fig. 22) into six equal parts (this number will of course vary with the required number of sides of the polygon)

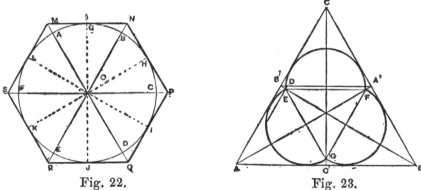

Fig. 22.   Fig. 23.

Fig. 22.—Polygon described about a Circle; Fig. 23.—Semicircles inscribed within Triangle.

and draw radii from o to A, B, C, D, E, F, producing them beyond the circle. Bisect the angles thus formed in lines terminating at G, H, I, J, K, L. Draw tangents to each of these radii. To do this, at the ends G, H, I, etc., of the lines last drawn, erect perpendiculars (Problem 3, p. 28) as M, N. These tangents, meeting in the produced radii A, B, C, D, E, and F, will form the required polygon about the circle. It is only necessary to go through this operation once in the present figure. The tangent drawn at G will cut the two radii o A and o B in M and N. From o, with radius o M or o N, describe a circle cutting the radii o C, o D, o E, and o F in P, Q, R, S. Join these points, and a hexagon will be constructed about the circle.

To inscribe within a given equilateral triangle three equal semicircles, having their diameters adjacent and equal. PROBLEM 21.—Let A B C (Fig. 23) be the equilateral triangle. Bisect the angles of the triangle by lines A A′ B B′, and C C′. Join A′ B′, and on this line describe a semicircle touching two sides of the triangle.

To avoid confusion of lines, this semicircle is omitted in the figure, one point only (D) where it would cut B′ A′ being shown. From D draw a line parallel to C A, cutting B B′ in E; from E draw a line parallel to B A, cutting A A′ in F. Draw F G, parallel to

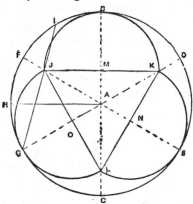

Fig. 24.—Three Semicircles inscribed within Circle.

C A. Join G and E by a line parallel to B C. Then E F, F G and G E will be the adjacent diameters of three semicircles which will touch the triangle A B C.

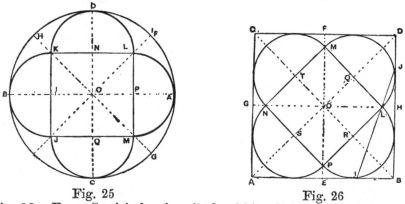

Fig. 25   Fig. 26

Fig. 25.—Four Semicircles inscribed within Circle; Fig. 26.—Four Semicircles inscribed within Square.

To inscribe in a given circle three equal semicircles, having their diameters adjacent. PROBLEM 22.—By Problem 7 (p. 29), find A the centre of the circle (Fig. 24). Draw the diameter B C, and from B and C set off the radius of the circle round the circumference, thus dividing it into six equal parts in E, C, G, F, B, D Draw E F and G D. Draw the radius A H at right angles to B C. From F set off F I equal to F H. From I draw a line to G cutting

E F in J. From A set off A K and A L equal to A J. Join J K, K L, and L J, which will give the diameters of the three required semicircles, the centres of which will be at M, N, and O.

To inscribe within a circle four equal semicircles, having their diameters adjacent. PROBLEM 23.—Draw two diameters A B and C D (Fig. 25), at right angles to each other, intersecting in O. Bisect the quadrants by E F and G H. Bisect O B in I. Draw a line through I parallel to C D, cutting E F in J and G H in K. Draw K L and J M parallel to A B, and join M L. Then the sides of the square J K L M will be the adjacent diameters of the required semicircles, of which I, N, P, and Q will be the centres, and I B the radius. This method can also be used to inscribe within a given square four equal semicircles, each touching one side of the

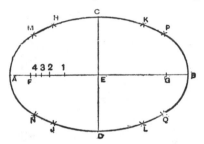

Fig. 27.—First Geometrical Method of Drawing Ellipse.

square, and having their diameters adjacent. Draw the diagonals of the square, and, with the point of intersection as centre, inscribe a circle within the square, and proceed as directed above.

To inscribe within a given square four equal semicircles, each touching two sides of the square, and having their diameters adjacent. PROBLEM 24.—Let A B C D (Fig. 26) be the given square. Draw the diagonals A D and B C, intersecting in O. Through O draw E F and G H parallel to A C and A B. Bisect E B in I, and D H in J. Draw I J, cutting G H in L. From O, on the diagonals set off O M, O N, and O P, equal to O L. Join L M, M N, N P, and P L, and a square will be constructed the sides of which will be parallel to the diagonals of the original square; these diagonals intersect the sides of the square L M N P in Q, R, S, and T. These points will be the centres for the required semicircles, the radius of which will equal Q L.

To draw an ellipse, the major and minor axes (or diameters) being given. PROBLEM 25.—The ellipse may be defined as a closed curve, such that the sum of the distances of any point in the curve from two points inside the curve is constant. Each of the two points inside is known as a focus, and the straight line joining them and bounded by the figure is the major axis, as A B (Fig. 27). The line which is seen to bisect the major axis at right angles, and which is bounded by the curve, is known as the minor axis, as at C D, Fig. 27.

Geometrical Method 1.—Draw the two given axes A B and C D mutually perpendicular and bisecting at E, as in Fig. 27. With the distance A E or E B as radius, and with D or C as centre, cut the axis A B in F and G. These are the foci. Between E and F mark any number of points; these may be spaced in any convenient manner, but will be found more useful if they are placed nearer together as they approach F. Then from centre F, radius

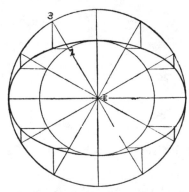

Fig. 28.—Second Geometrical Method of Drawing Ellipse.

A 1, strike arcs above and below A B, and from centre G, radius B 1, similarly describe arcs that cut the former ones in the points H and J. With the same radii the points K and L can be found. In the same way, with radii equal to A 2 and B 2, the points M, N, P, and Q can then be determined. A number of points are then found in a similar way so as to enable the curve to be drawn by hand.

Geometrical Method 2.—On the axes describe circles as shown in Fig. 28. Then by radii divide the circles into any number of equal parts, and where these radii cut the outer circle drop vertical lines to meet horizontals drawn from the cutting points of similar radii with the inner circle. Thus, taking the case of radius E 1 3, a vertical line from 3 meets a horizontal from 1 in the point F. The points thus found can be connected by curves by hand to form the ellipse.

Mechanical Method 1.—In Fig. 29, A B and C D are the axes crossing at E, and F and G are the foci. Now fasten pins at F and G, and connect them by a string, the length of which is equal to the sum of the dotted lines F C and C G. Pull the string tight by a pencil, as shown, and swing it round to form the curve at both top and bottom.

Mechanical Method 2.—Draw the two axes A B and C D (Fig. 30), bisecting one another at right angles at E. Then, upon a strip of card, mark from a point E' half the width and half the length of the figure, as E' C', E' B'. Now, keeping the points B' and C' upon the lines A B and C D, move the strip round a short distance, and after each movement mark a point at E'. A series of points may thus be obtained, and a curve drawn through them to form the figure required. This method is sometimes

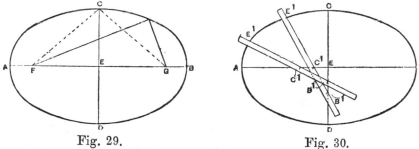

Fig. 29.　　　　　　　　Fig. 30.

Fig. 29.—First Mechanical Method of Drawing Ellipse; Fig. 30.—
Second Mechanical Method of Drawing Ellipse.

convenient when working elbow and similar patterns; a number of confusing construction lines are thereby avoided.

Approximate Method 1.—Draw the axes A B and C D (Fig. 31), intersecting at E, and mark the length and width upon them. Next mark the width C D from A along A B, as at F, and divide the difference between length and width into three equal parts, as 1, 2, B. From E mark a distance equal to two of these divisions on each side of the centre line to give the points P and P^1. Using the distance P P^1 as radius, and P and P^1 as alternate centres, describe arcs intersecting at R and R^1. Draw lines through R P, R^1 P^1, etc., as shown, and then using P and P^1 as centres, with radius P^1 A, or P B, describe arcs to join the lines that pass through the centres P and P^1. Use R and R^1 as alternate centres, and with radius R D or R^1 C, draw the side arcs to join the end arcs, and so complete the figure.

Approximate Method 2.—Place the two diameters or axes A B and C D (Fig. 32) at right angles, and intersecting each other at their middle point E. From B on the line A B set off B F equal to E C. From E set off E G on E C equal to E F, and draw G F, bisecting it in I. From F set off F J equal to F I, and draw J K parallel to F G. From E set off E L and E M equal to E J, and complete the square J K L M, producing the sides beyond J and L. The angles of the square are the centres from which the elliptical figure may be drawn. From K and M, with radius K D or M C, describe arcs cutting the produced sides of the square in N O and P Q. From J and L, with radius L A or J B, describe arcs joining N P and O Q.

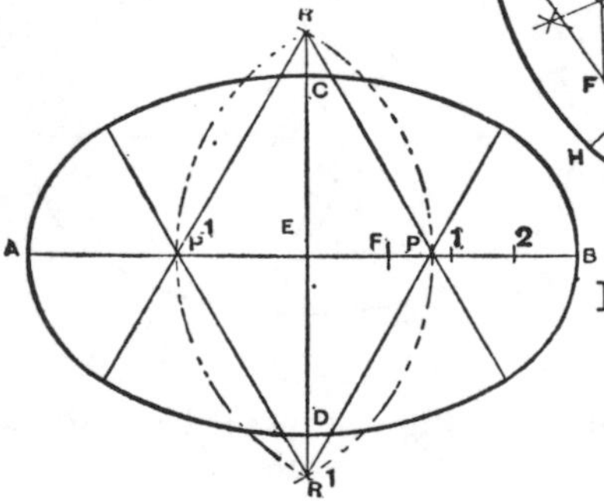

Fig. 31.—First Approximate Method of Drawing Ellipse.

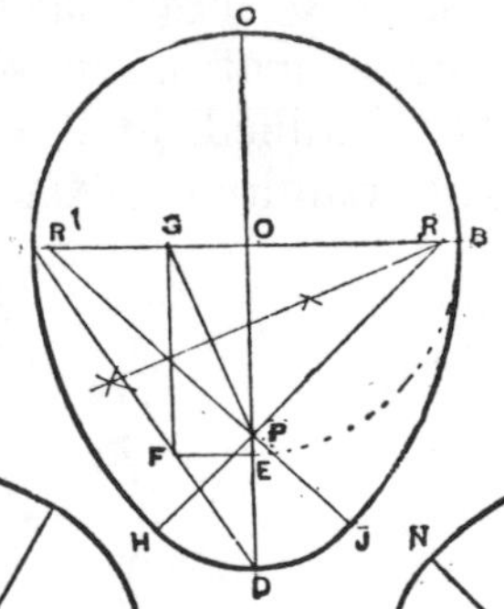

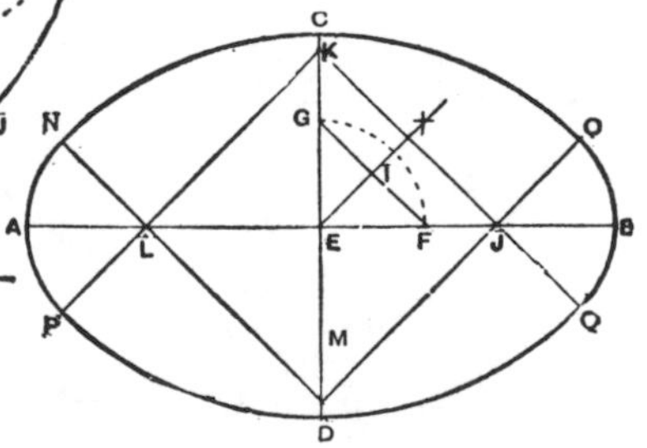

Fig. 32.—Second Approximate Method of Drawing Ellipse.

Fig. 33.—Egg-shaped Oval.

To draw an egg-shaped oval where the length and width are given. PROBLEM 26.—Draw two lines, intersecting at right angles at o (Fig. 33), and mark the width of the oval as A B. Use o as centre, and with radius to A or B, describe a semicircle. From C mark the full length of the oval at D, and join A and D by a straight line. With o B as radius, and o as centre, draw the dotted quarter-circle B E, and from E draw a line at right angles to C D to cut the diagonal A D at F. From F draw a line parallel to C D to cut A B at G. Mark the length A G from D along D C to give the point P. Join G to P, and bisect G P, producing the line of bisection to cut A B at R. Make R¹ o equal to R o, and draw lines from R and R¹ to pass through P. Then, using R and R¹ as alternate centres, and with radius R A or R¹ B, describe arcs from A and B to H and J. Use P as centre, and P D as radius, and describe the arc from H to J to complete the figure.

CHAPTER III.

GEOMETRICAL CONSTRUCTION AND DEVELOPMENT OF SOLID FIGURES.

THE methods of representing solid objects may now be considered. By the term solid, however, is meant such as are apparently so. Thus a cube does not necessarily mean a block of stone or wood, but possibly an object of the same form made of sheet metal, and therefore appearing solid. A sectional view shows whether an object is solid or hollow; in the latter case it shows also the thickness of the material of which the object is made.

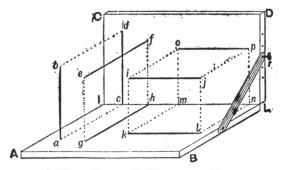

Fig. 34.—Plans and Elevations of Lines on Horizontal and Vertical Planes.

If two planes or surfaces are placed at right angles to each other, to form as it were a floor and a wall, the floor A B (Fig. 34) may, in projection, be called the horizontal plane and the wall C D the vertical plane. Now place a piece of wire in an upright position, $a\,b$, then the part whereon the wire rests is called the horizontal projection or plan, and if projectors or lines were carried directly back from its extremities parallel to the plane A B and perpendicular to the plane C D until they cut the vertical plane in c and d, the line $c\,d$ would be the vertical projection or elevation of the wire.

Similarly, if a wire $e\,f$ be placed at right angles to the vertical plane, the part f whereon it rests is the elevation, being the

view which would be obtained if the model were placed on an
exact level with the eye, the point *e* being immediately opposite
the spectator, so that the end only of the wire could be seen. If
now perpendiculars are dropped from *e* and *f* until they meet
the horizontal plane in *g* and *h*, the line uniting *g* and *h* will
be the plan of the wire, or the view obtained by looking down
on it.   Further, if we suppose a line *ij* to be suspended in
space, perpendiculars dropped from its extremities to cut the
horizontal plane will give the plan *kl*.   Then, if the lines be
drawn from *k* and *l* to meet the vertical plane in *m* and *n*, and

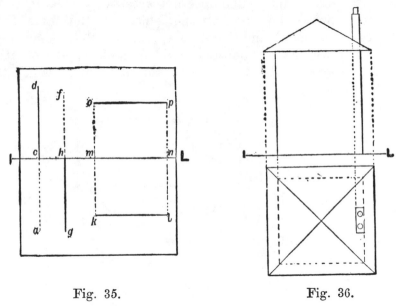

Fig. 35.   Fig. 36.

Fig. 35.—Plans and Elevation of Lines; Fig. 36.—Plan and Elevation of Small Lodge.

perpendiculars be raised from these points, intersected by lines
drawn from the ends of the wire parallel to *km* and *ln*, the
points *o* and *p* will be obtained, and the line joining these will
be the elevation of the wire *ij*.

In the model illustrated by Fig. 34 the vertical and horizontal
planes are connected by hinges, and are kept at right angles to
each other by means of a brass loop. If now the wires be
removed and the pin *r* be withdrawn so as to allow the plane
C D to fall backward, the two planes of projection will form one
surface separated only by the line I L (Fig. 35), and the plans

and elevations will be seen in their respective positions on the two planes.

The line separating the two planes is called the intersecting line, and is therefore lettered I L. It is very often marked by the letters X Y.

It must be pointed out that the "plan" of an object does not mean merely the piece of ground it stands upon, but the space it overhangs as well. Thus, the piece of ground on which the small lodge (Fig. 36) would stand is represented by the dotted square in the plan, whilst the true space which the building covers or overhangs is represented by the outer square.

It will be seen that in all the figures shown in Figs. 34 and 35 the lengths of the plans and the heights of the elevations are the same as the lengths and heights of the objects they represent—thus $c\,d$ is the same length as $a\,b$, and $k\,l$ and $o\,p$ are the same length as $i\,j$. This is not always so, lengths and heights being dependent on the position or angle in which the subject to be drawn is placed.

Before treating of the changes which the projections of lines undergo by alteration of position of the lines, it is necessary that the terms used to define such positions should be understood. In Fig. 34 the line $a\,b$ stands upright on the floor of the model, and as its distance from the wall is the same throughout its entire length, it is said to be at right angles to the horizontal plane and parallel to the vertical plane.

Similarly, the line $e\,f$ is said to be at right angles to the vertical and parallel to the horizontal plane ; and it is evident that the line $i\,j$ is parallel to both planes.

It will be seen that whilst the plan of a line when standing upright is a mere point (a, Fig. 35), the plan of the same line when placed horizontally—as $k\,l$—is the full length of the original. To account for this difference, let the position of the wire be perfectly upright to commence with. Then its plan will be the point a, and its elevation the line $b\,c$ in Fig. 37.

Now, if this wire be made to work on a hinge joint at b, and if the end c be moved from left to right, as from c to d, the end d being kept the same distance from the wall of the model, the wire may still be parallel to the vertical, but inclined to the horizontal plane. As shown, it is inclined at 60°, but it may, of course, be inclined at any angle.

To find the plan of this wire, draw a line from a parallel to

I L: From *d* drop a perpendicular to cut this line, then *a e* is the plan of *b d* in the position in which it is now placed—viz. parallel to the vertical and inclined at 60° to the horizontal plane. If the movement were continued until *d* reached *f*, the wire would then be parallel to both planes. The plan would be the line *a g*.

Now suppose the wire fixed in this slanting position as far as its inclination to the horizontal plane is concerned; if the whole hinge is made to rotate on a pivot, so that without altering the slant the end *d* may be turned forward, the line will then be inclined or slanting to both planes.

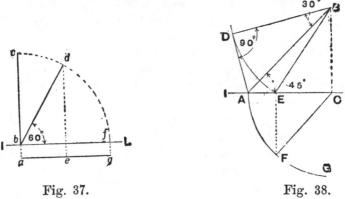

Fig. 37.   Fig. 38.

Fig. 37.—Plan and Elevation of Line; Fig. 38.—Projections of Line inclined to both Planes.

To draw the projections of a line inclined to both planes. PROBLEM 27.—Suppose that the line is to be inclined 45° to the horizontal plane and 30° to the vertical plane. Draw a horizontal line I L (Fig. 38), and at any point A draw the line A B so that the angle B A L equals 45°. Make A B equal to the true length of the line, and drop a perpendicular from B to cut I L in C. With C as centre, C A as radius, describe a portion of a circle A G as shown. Next from B set out the line B D, making the angle D B A equal to 30°, and at A erect the line A D so that the angle A D B equals 90°. Then, with B as centre, B D as radius, describe an arc of a circle to cut I L in E. A line joining E B is the required elevation of the line. To determine the plan, from E drop a line perpendicular to I L; this line will cut the arc A G at the point shown by F. Join F and C by a straight line, and then F C is the required plan.

To determine the true length and inclinations of a line, its projections being given. PROBLEM. 28.—Let A B, C D (Fig. 39) be the plan and elevation respectively of the line in question. Draw the projectors C A and D B, and at A and B drop perpendiculars, making A G equal to C E and B H to D F. Then join G H to show the true length of the line. To determine the inclination to the horizontal plane at any point in the line G H as at G, draw a line G J parallel to A B. The angle J G H is the required inclination. To determine the inclination to the vertical plane, determine the true length K L as before, making

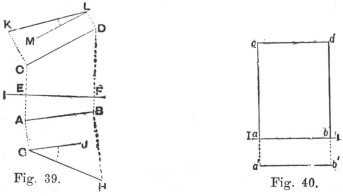

Fig. 39.   Fig. 40.

Fig. 39.—Determining Length and Inclinations of Line. Fig. 40.—
Plan and Elevation of Rectangle.

C K and D L equal to E A and F B respectively. Then draw L M parallel to C D to give the required angle.

The laws that govern the projection of single lines govern also the delineation of planes, which are flat surfaces bounded by lines. Let *a*, *b*, *c*, *d* (Fig. 40) be a metal plate, the surface of which is parallel to the vertical and perpendicular to the horizontal plane. Its plan will then be the line *a′ b′*. If, now, this plane be turned, so as to be at right angles to both planes, its plan—that is, the line on which it would stand—will be *a′ b′* (Fig. 41), and its elevation the line *a″ c″*. Now, let this plane rotate on the line *a″ c″* as a door on its hinges, until *b′* in the plan reaches *b″*, then a perpendicular drawn from *b′* will give the rectangle *a″ c″ b‴ d‴*, which will be the projection of the plane, when perpendicular to the horizontal and inclined to the vertical plane, the height remaining unaltered. The other rectangles show the projections of the plane when further rotated.

In Fig. **42** the plane again rests on the ground or horizontal plane on *a b*, its edge *b d* only being visible in the elevation ; but this edge hides the opposite one, which is parallel to it, and therefore the points *a* and *c″* are immediately at the back of, or "beyond," *b* and *d″*. Now rotate the plane on *a b*, as in closing a box-lid or trap-door. Then the more the plane is lowered the longer the plan will become, as shown at *e* and *f*.

Notwithstanding the slanting direction which the plane has

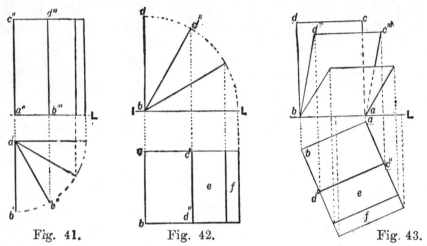

Fig. 41.　　　　Fig. 42.　　　　Fig. 43.

Figs. 41 and 42.—Plans and Elevations of Rectangle ; Fig. 43.—Projections of Rectangle inclined to both Planes.

assumed in relation to the horizontal plane, it still remains at right angles to the vertical plane. This is shown in the plan, where the lines *a b* and *c″ d″*, which represent the upper and lower edges of the plane, are perpendicular to ɪ ʟ. Let the plane be so placed that it is inclined to both planes of projection. This will be done by rotating the plan, carefully lettered as in Fig. 43. Then perpendiculars drawn from each of the points intersected by horizontal lines from the corresponding points in the elevation will give the required projection. The process is so plainly shown in the elevation that further explanation is deemed unnecessary.

In Fig. 44 A B C D is the plan of a cube and E F G H is the elevation, which in the present position of the cube is the same shape as the plan. For it will be evident that since the cube consists entirely of squares at right angles to each other, the piece of ground the object stands upon must be a square, and also that the side standing on A B is parallel to the vertical plane, and hence its elevation is the square E F G H.

In Fig. 45 the object is shown rotated so that one angle, A, faces the spectator, and thus in the elevation two sides are visible, neither of them, however, appearing of its real width, whilst the height remains unchanged.

Figs. 46 and 47 show plans and elevations of a triangular prism. In Fig. 46 one face is turned towards the spectator, and thus, as it is parallel to one vertical plane, the elevation is simply a rectangle. Fig. 47 shows the same prism when turned round, so that the face parallel to the vertical plane is at the back, and one

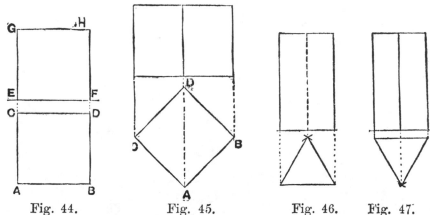

Fig. 44.   Fig. 45.   Fig. 46.   Fig. 47.

Fig. 44.—Plan and Elevation of Cube; Fig. 45.—Plan and Elevation of Cube at Angle to Vertical Plane; Figs. 46 and 47.—Plans and Elevations of Triangular Prism.

edge facing the spectator; the elevation is thus two rectangles, the boundary line, however, being the outline of the rectangle, which is parallel to the vertical plane.

It has already been said that an object apparently solid is not necessarily so, and it is a most important part of the work of the metal plate worker to know the exact shape to which the sheet metal is to be cut, so that when bent and united, the object required may be formed. This portion of the subject is called the development of surfaces.

To develop a cube. PROBLEM 29.—Construct the square *a b c d* (Fig. 48), representing the base or any one side of the cube. Produce the sides of this square to *e, f, g, h, i, j, k,* and *l,* and construct the squares *a e f b, b g h d, d l k c,* and *c j i a.* At *k l* (or at any other of the external lines) construct the square *k l n m,*

D

which will complete the development, for it will be seen that if the squares *a e f b*, *b g h d*, *d l k c*, and *e j i a* were bent upwards, they would form four walls of a box, of which *a b c d* would be the bottom, and that the square *k l n m* would fold over and form the top or lid, parallel to *a b c d*.

To develop a triangular prism. PROBLEM 30.—It is clear that this object (Fig. 49) consists of three rectangular faces and two triangular ends. Therefore draw the three rectangles A B D C, C D F E, and E F H G, and at the ends of one of them draw the equilateral triangles A C J and B D I, which will complete the required figure.

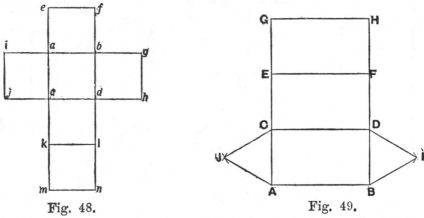

Fig. 48.   Fig. 49.

Fig. 48.—Cube developed ; Fig. 49.—Triangular Prism developed.

To find the true shape of a section or cutting caused by a plane passing through a square prism. PROBLEM 31.—*Example* 1.—Let *a b* (Fig. 50) show the direction of the plane of section which would cut through the diagonal *a c* of the top and the angle *d* of the bottom. Draw the dotted lines *a h* and *b f* at right angles to the line of section, and at any point in this line draw *f g* parallel to *a b*. The section plane, in passing through *a′ c* in plan, cuts the object in the widest part. Therefore, if the eye be carried down from *a* in the elevation to *a′ c* in the plan, it will be seen that the real width on each side of the centre *e* is *e a′* and *e c*. Therefore, if these lengths be set off on each side of *g* in the section line as *g h* and *g j*, and the points joined to *f*, then *j f h* will be the true section.

Example 2.—In Fig. 51 the section plane passes from one angle of the top to the opposite angle of the bottom, cutting through the middle of the two edges. The length will of course be equal to that of the section line, and the width across the middle will be equal to the diagonal of the square, as at *a c* in Fig. 50 ; and from this width the figure narrows to a point both at top and bottom.

Example 3.—In Fig. 52 the section plane passes from a line connecting the middle points of the two adjacent edges of the top to a similar line on the two opposite edges of the base. The width of the section at its middle will be equal to the diagonal of the square base, and at the top and bottom it will be equal to *g h*. It is usual to cover sections with lines at 45° to the vertical or to the central line of the figure.

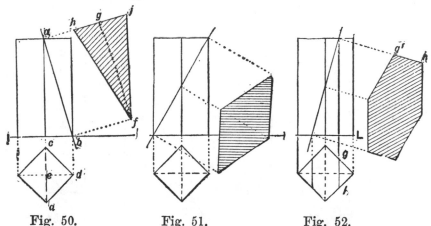

Fig. 50.   Fig. 51.   Fig. 52.
Figs. 50—52.—Projections of Square Prism showing Sections.

To determine the development of a square prism. PROBLEM 32.—The mere development will of course be easily understood, since it is similar to that of a cube, four of the faces being elongated instead of being square. The object of the present problem, however, is to show the section line on the development, thus enabling the workman to cut the metal out whilst flat, so that when bent, not only the general shape of the object may be formed, but the aperture caused by the section, and the covering of that aperture (which will be the true section), may be the result.

Example 1.—In Fig. 50 the section plane enters at the top, on the diagonal *a c*. Therefore, draw the diagonal *a c* in the square *a b c d* (Fig 53) representing the top of the present development. Now it will be clear that *a* is one of the points from which the section line is to be drawn, and also that when the development is folded into its proper form, c' would reach c ; c' is thus another of the points of the section line, and a' will be the third. Draw $a\,a'\,c'$, which will be the line of section. The covering for this aperture will then be an isosceles triangle, of which $a\,c'$ is the base, and $a\,a'$ and $c'\,a'$ the sides.

In a material which may be bent, it may be economical to make the whole development in one piece, and therefore the present method is shown. From a', with radius $a'\,c'$, describe an arc and from c', with radius $a\,c$, describe an arc cutting the previous arc in e. Join $e\,a'$, $a'\,c'$, and $c'\,e$. Then the triangle $c'\,e\,a'$ is the required covering of the aperture.

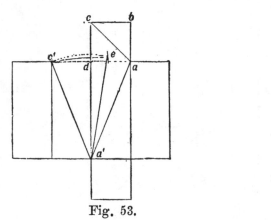 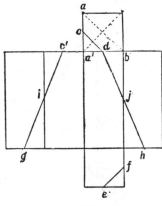

Fig. 53.   Fig. 54.

Fig. 53.—Square Prism developed ; Fig. 54.—Square Prism developed.

Example 2.—In Fig. 54 is another development of the same prism, showing the section caused by a plane passing from the middle points of two adjacent sides of the top to a line joining two corresponding points in the opposite edges of the base, as in Fig. 52.

Having drawn the general form of the development (Fig. 54), draw the diagonal $a\,b$, and the line $c\,d$ parallel to it, from points in the middle of the sides of the square. Draw a corresponding line at the opposite angle of the square representing the other end of the prism, namely, $e\,f$.

From a' set off $a'\,c'$ equal to $a'\,c$, and find the corresponding points, g and h, on the edges of the base. Draw $c'\,g$ passing through i, the middle joint of an edge, and draw $d\,h$ passing through j, and these will be the section lines. The true section is shaded in Fig. 52.

To determine the developments and sections of elbows of square piping. PROBLEM 33.—Fig. 55 shows the plan and elevation of a piece of square metal piping. When the plane of the section passes from one side to the other at 45° the section will be a rectangle the length of which is equal to the section line, whilst the width corresponds with the side of the pipe.

Now if, when such a pipe has been cut through at 45°, the upper portion is turned round, rotating as it were on a pin fixed in the centre of the section, the two parts meeting on the line *c d* will form an elbow joint.

In the present example, the joint forms a right angle, because the section line was made at 45° (that is, half a right angle), but

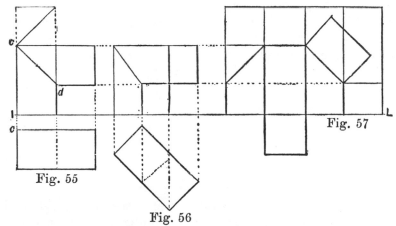

Fig. 55

Fig. 56

Fig. 57

Figs. 55—57.—Projections and Development of Square Piping.

an elbow of any angle may be formed by the same method, the angle of the section line always being half the angle required to be formed by the joint.

Fig. 56 is a projection of the object when placed at an angle to the vertical plane. To draw this figure, place the plan at the required angle to the intersecting line, and draw perpendiculars from all its angles.

It has already been pointed out that when an object is rotated horizontally without its inclination being altered, its height remains unchanged. This may be frequently seen in the objects around us ; for instance, a door, however much it may be moved on the line of the hinges, remains the same height. Thus, then, this elbow joint, so rotated, is the same height as when its side was parallel to the vertical plane, as in Fig. 55. It is only necessary, therefore, to draw horizontals from Fig. 55 to cut the perpendiculars drawn from the angles of Fig. 56 to complete the projection.

Fig. 57 is the development with the shape of the section attached. Set out, in the first place, the four sides of the prism with the ends, one only of which is shown. On this development, draw across one side a horizontal line from *c* in Fig. 55. From *d* draw a horizontal line, which will give the height of the right-hand face. Join the points thus determined by oblique lines, on one of which construct the rectangle representing the true section, and this would form the lid, if one part were formed into a common coal-scuttle, as shown. This is made quite clear by reference to the general view of the coal-scuttle, Fig. 58.

Figs. 59 to 61 give the method of obtaining the development and section line of a square pipe cut so as to form a double elbow. A B D C (Fig. 59) is the plan, and E F H G is the side elevation of the pipe.

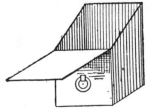

Fig. 58.—Coal-scuttle.

Draw I J and K L, the section lines as seen in the side eleva- tion. It will be clear that if the middle part, I J L K, were removed, the upper part, G H K L, could be brought down upon E F J I, and form a straight pipe as in the last example, and thus that the change is caused merely by rotating the middle piece, I J L K, as on a pin in the centre of each section, the upper and lower parts remaining vertical during the operation. This will be easily understood if a similar model be made of three pieces of wood. When, therefore, this middle piece is rotated in the manner described, the lines M and N of Fig. 59 will take the positions of M′ and N′ in Fig. 60, whilst the lower portion, E′ F′ J′ I′, will occupy precisely the same position as in Fig. 59, as will also the upper part, K′ L′ H′ G′, excepting that it is moved towards the right side and lowered.

Fig. 61 is the development showing the section line, which, being constructed in precisely the same method as Fig. 57, does not require further explanation.

To determine the development and section of a hexagonal prism.
PROBLEM 34.—Fig. 62 shows the plan and elevation of a hexagonal prism, to be cut at an angle of 45° by a plane represented by the line A B. The method of projecting the elevation from the plan does not now require explanation, so the method of obtaining the true form of the section will be shown.

It will be clear that C and D in the elevation represent not only the two points so lettered, but two lying behind them on the back face ; thus, C and D in the elevation correspond with c and d in the plan, and it will be seen that c' and d' lie directly at the back of these. Thus, then, whilst the length of the section will be equal to A B, its width will be c c' or d d'.

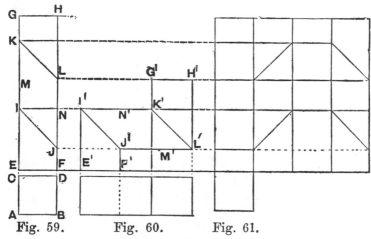

Fig. 59.   Fig. 60.   Fig. 61.

Figs. 59—61.—Projections and Development of Square Pipe Double Elbow.

From A and B draw lines at right angles to A B, and from any point A' draw A' B' parallel to A B. Now, from C and D draw lines at right angles to A B, cutting A' B' in 1 and 2. On these lines set off from 1 and 2 the widths corresponding with c 3 c' or d 4 d' in the plan—namely, e 1 f and g 2 h. Join A', g, e, B', f, h, A', and the figure thus completed will be the true section.

In Fig. 63 the prism is represented as rotated on its axis, so that one edge faces the spectator, whilst in Fig. 62 the side c d was parallel to the vertical plane of projection. Horizontal lines drawn from A, B, C, D will give the view of the section in this, figure ; but it must be understood that this section is not the true one, the form being apparently shorter, owing to the position of the section, which, of course, slants backward from the lower point.

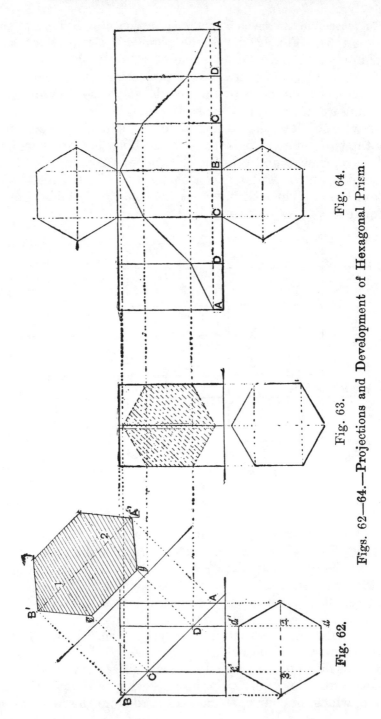

Fig. 64.

Fig. 63.

Fig. 62.

Figs. 62—64.—Projections and Development of Hexagonal Prism.

Fig. 64 is the development of the prism, and on this the section line is shown. The latter is, as before, obtained by drawing horizontal lines from the points B, C, D, A in the elevation, to cut corresponding perpendiculars in the development, the constructional horizontal lines being shown dotted.

As an exercise on the foregoing, let it be required to project a pyramid the base and sides of which are equilateral triangles. Such a solid is called a " tetrahedron."

A B C (Fig. 65) is the plan and $c\,a'$ the width of the elevation. Now, $a\,c$ would be the height of the object only if the three

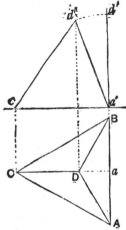

Fig. 65.—Projection of Triangular Pyramid.

triangular sides stood upright on their edges A B, B C, C A. But they slant inward until the apexes meet in a point, which, as all the sides are equal, will be at D, the centre of the plan. Therefore, to determine the elevation, draw a perpendicular from D and another at a'.

Mark on the perpendicular $a'\,d'$ the height $a'\,c$. This perpendicular will be the edge elevation of the side. Then from a', with the radius $a'\,d'$, describe an arc cutting the perpendicular drawn from D in d'', which will be the apex. Join $a'\,d''$ and $c\,d''$, which will complete the elevation.

The apex does not appear to be over the middle of the solid in the elevation, because $a'\,d''$ is the projection of a face of the triangle, whilst the line $c\,d''$ is the projection of the edge C D. This appears plainly in the plan, where C D is longer than D a ; yet D is in the centre of the triangle.

To determine the projections and development of square and hexagonal pyramids. PROBLEM 35.—Fig. 66 gives the plan and elevation of a square pyramid, when the two edges A B and C D of the base are parallel to the vertical plane. The position of the apex is found, as in Fig. 65, by marking on a perpendicular the slant altitude of the side, and then inclining this elevation of the side until it cuts the axis in *e.* Fig. 67 shows (in dotted lines) the plan and elevation of the same pyramid, when one of the diagonals of the plan is parallel to the vertical plane.

Let it be required to draw the plan of the pyramid when resting on the angle at *d*, Fig. 67, the plane of the base being at an angle of 30° with the horizontal plane.

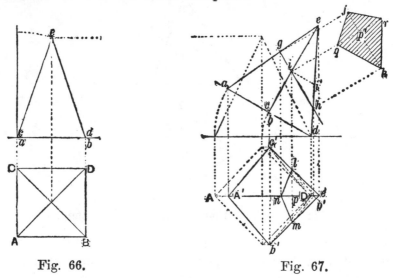

Fig. 66.   Fig. 67.

Figs. 66 and 67.—Plans and Elevations of Square Pyramid.

Place the elevation *a d e* (Fig. 67) at the required angle, and project the square that forms the base of the pyramid. In doing this, it will be seen that the base turns on *d*, *a* being raised; thus, the diagonal *d a* of the elevation is in the plan reduced in length to D A′, the other diagonal *b′ c′* retaining its full width. Produce the diagonal A D, and drop a perpendicular from the apex (*e*) to cut this line in *e′*, the plan of the apex. Join this point to the points of the plan of the base, and so complete the plan.

To find the true shape of the section on the line *g h*, draw lines from *g*, *i*, and *h* at right angles to *g h*, and draw *j k* parallel to that line ; *j k* will be the length of the section. From *g, i*, and *h,* draw perpendiculars respectively cutting the plan in *n, l m,* and *o'.* Join these points, and a plan of the section will be obtained.

On each side of *p'* in the upper figure, set off the length *p m* or *p l* of the plan to make the points *q* and *r.* Join *j q, q k, k r,* and *r j,* and the true section will be completed.

To draw the development of this pyramid (Fig. 68), with a radius equal to the true height of one of the sides of the pyramid describe an arc. Draw the radius *e a.* From *a* mark on the arc

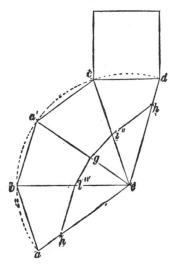

Fig. 68.—Development of Square Pyramid.

the chords *a b, b a', a' c,* and *c d,* equal to the edges of the base. Join these points, and from each of them draw lines to *e.* On either of the lines, such as *c d,* construct a square for the base of the pyramid; and this will complete the development.

It remains, however, to show on this development the line of section. Mark on *a' e* the length *a y* of the elevation (Fig. 67). From *i* (Fig. 67) draw *i i'* parallel to *a d.* From *c* and *b* (Fig. 68), set off on *c e* and *b e* the lengths *c i'''* and *b l''* equal to *d i'* (Fig. 67).

On *a e* and *d e* (Fig. 68), mark off the length *d h,* taken from Fig. 67. Join *h, l'', g, i''',* and *h* by straight lines to obtain the line of section required.

Fig. 69 is the plan and elevation of a hexagonal pyramid, placed so that one of the edges faces the spectator, two of the sides of the base (B C and E F) being at right angles to the vertical plane of projection. The elevation is cut by a line G H parallel to the base, and it is required to find the true section of the pyramid when cut by a plane, of which the line G H is the elevation.

It will be clear that in this position each of the side lines in the elevation represents two edges.

All sections of this pyramid, parallel to the base, are regular hexagons; therefore a perpendicular drawn from I to cut the plans of the edges E O and F O will give $i\, i'$, one side of the true section; and lines drawn from i and i' parallel to E D and F A will be two more, and thus the whole plan may be completed.

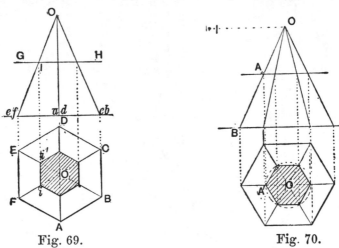

Fig. 69.　　　　　　　　Fig. 70.

Figs. 69 and 70.—Plans, Elevations, and Sections of Hexagonal Pyramid.

Similarly, Fig. 70 gives the plan and elevation of the same pyramid when rotated on its axis, so that two faces are parallel to the vertical plane. Here the section line is seen cutting the elevation of the edge of the pyramid in A, and a perpendicular dropped to cut the plan of the edge in A' gives the radius of a circle that will contain the true section; from the centre therefore, with radius O A', describe this circle, and this, cutting the other five radii of the hexagon, will give points on the hexagon that will be the true section.

For the development of this pyramid, the line B O (Fig. 70) is the true length of the edges of the pyramid; therefore, from any point as O (Fig. 71), with radius B O, describe an arc and set off on it six distances equal to the side of the hexagon forming the plan. From each of the points draw a line to O, which will complete the development. Now on each of these lines set off from o the length O A taken from Fig. 70. Join the points to obtain the section line, thus completing the figure.

To determine the development of a right cone and of a right cone cut elliptically. PROBLEM 36.—Fig. 72 shows the plan and elevation of the cone, with A B as the line of section. First draw the plan of the section, divide the circumference of the plan into any number of equal parts, C, D, E, F, G, H, I, and H', G', F', E', and D', and draw radii. Project these points on to the base of the elevation of the cone, and from C', D'', etc., draw lines to the apex J'.

The diagram up to this point represents a cone, on the slanting surface of which straight lines have been drawn. The line E'' J' in the elevation is therefore represented by E J in the plan, and

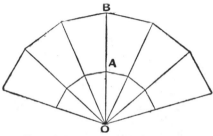

Fig. 71.—Development of Hexagonal Pyramid.

thus the plan of any point marked on E'' J' must fall somewhere on the radius E J. The section line A B cuts through the lines drawn to the apex of the cone in the points d', e', f' g', and h.' From points A and B draw perpendiculars cutting the diameter C I in plan in a and b, and from d', e', ƒ, g', and h' in the elevation, draw perpendiculars cutting the similarly lettered radii of the plan. In plan draw the curve that unites e, d, a, d'', e'', and also the curve uniting g, h, b, h'', g''. It will at once be seen that these two curves form the ends of the ellipse that is the plan of the section, but that points are wanted on F F' in order to complete the figure. A perpendicular cannot be drawn from the point f in the elevation to cut the radius F J in the plan, because the radii J F, J F', are but portions of the same perpendicular on which the point f' is situated, and therefore no intersection could be obtained. Now the line F'' J', though appearing perpendicular to X Y when looked at in its present position, would, if looked at from K in the direction of the arrow, be seen to make the same angle with the horizontal plane as I' J'.

If, then, the cone is rotated on its axis, the point f' will move to $f'f'$, and a perpendicular drawn from $f'f'$ will give ff in the plan. On turning back the cone to its original position, as

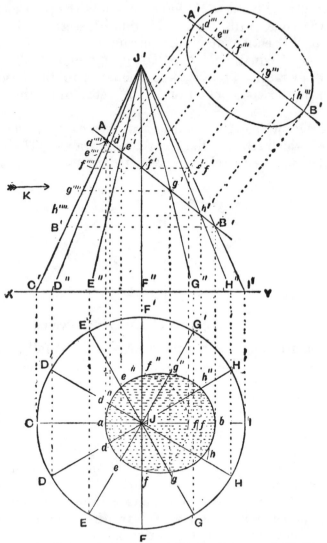

Fig. 72.—Projection and Section of Right Cone, and Right Cone cu Elliptically.

represented by drawing a quadrant from the centre of the plan with radius Jff, the quadrant will cut the radius J F in f, and J F' in f''. Join e and g, and e'' and g'' by curves passing through f and f''', to complete the plan of the section.

This, however, is not the true section, for it will be evident that the true length of the section is the line A to B. From these points then, and also from d', e', f' g', and h', draw lines at right angles to the section line, and draw A′ B′ parallel to it. On each side of the points d''', e''', f''', g''', h''', in the line A′ B′, set off the distances which the points similarly lettered are from C I in the plan, and these will give the points through which the curve of true section may be drawn.

To develop the entire cone, in Fig. 73 from any point, as J″, draw a line J″ c′ equal to J′ I′ in the elevation (Fig. 72), and with this length as radius describe an arc. On each side of c′ set off on this arc six equal distances c′ D, D E, etc., equal to C D, D E, etc., of Fig. 72. Join I and I′ to J″, and the sector thus formed will be the development of the cone.

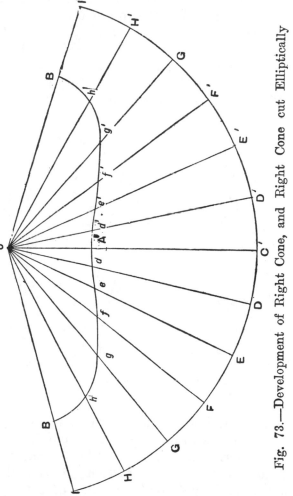

Fig. 73.—Development of Right Cone, and Right Cone cut Elliptically

To trace the line of section, draw lines to J″ from the points D, D′, E, E′, F, F′, etc., already marked on the arc I, I′. From the points d', e', f, g', h', and B in the section line A B (Fig. 72), draw lines parallel to the base of the cone, cutting the line c′ J′ in d''', e'''', f'''', g'''', h'''', and B′, Fig. 72. From c′ (Fig. 73), set off the length c′ A taken from Fig. 72. On the lines from D and D′ (Fig. 73) set off the length c' d'''' taken from Fig. 72, and proceed thus for the other points, transferring the lengths on c' j' (Fig. 72) to the lines similarly lettered in Fig. 73, and through the points thus obtained draw the curve B A' B. This is the line in which the material would be cut, so that when I' B and I B are brought together, a truncated cone may be formed, the section of which on the line A B (Fig. 72) will be the ellipse A' B'.

To set out the frustum of a right cone. PROBLEM 37.—*Method 1.*—For the frustum of a right cone that is of slight taper, use the short radius method. To do this, first draw a half elevation of the frustum of the cone to the dimensions required ; thus with o (Fig. 74) as centre, and radius equal to half the diameter of the

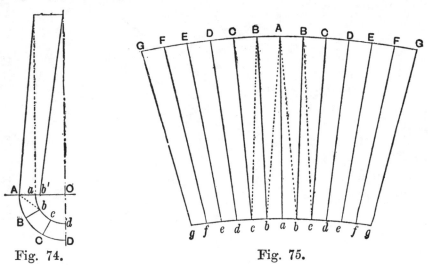

Fig. 74.   Fig. 75.

Figs. 74 and 75.—First Method of Setting out Frustum of Right Cone.

larger end, describe the quarter circle A D ; then, using the same centre, and with radius equal to half the diameter of the smaller end, describe the quarter circle a d, the two quadrants forming a quarter plan of the frustum. Divide the quarter circles into any suitable and similar number of equal parts, as A, B, C, D, and a, b, c, d, and join the division points by straight lines ; also join A to b, as shown ; this cross line will be the plan of a diagonal line joining A on the bottom of the frustum to b on the top. Mark the length A b along the ground line from o, and join b¹ to the top of the perpendicular which indicates the upright height ; this length will be the true length of the diagonal shown by A b on the plan. Commence the pattern by drawing a straight line, and make it equal in length to the slant of the frustum, as A a (Fig. 75). Now take the diagonal slant as radius, and using A as centre, describe arcs at $b\,b$; take the distance $a\,b$ (Fig. 74) as radius, and with a (Fig. 75) as centre, cut the arcs drawn at $b\,b$; the points found by the intersection of the arcs will fix the position of the points $b\,b$ on the pattern. Now, with $b\,b$ as centres and the length A a (Fig. 75) as radius, describe arcs at B B; take the division length A B (Fig. 74) as radius, and using A (Fig. 75) as centre, cut the arcs drawn at B B, and so fix the position of the points B B on the pattern. Repeat this construc-

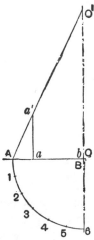

Fig. 76.—Second Method of Setting Out Frustum of Right Cone.

tion until the number of divisions on the pattern equals those on the complete circumference of the base of the frustum of the cone. Draw a curve through the intersecting arcs at the top and bottom of Fig. 75, and join G g, G g by straight lines to complete the pattern.

Method 2.—Mark half the diameter of the larger end upon a straight line, as A B (Fig. 76), and half the diameter (a b) of the smaller end from o along the same line. Erect perpendiculars from o and from a, and upon the latter mark the upright height of the frustum of the cone at a'. Draw a line from A through a' to meet the perpendicular at o'; this will show a half elevation of a right cone, which will contain the given frustum. Draw the quarter circle A 6 to form a quarter plan of the base of the cone. To draw the pattern, take the length A o' as radius, and describe

E

an arc of a circle; divide the quarter circle into a number of equal divisions, as 1, 2, 3, 4, 5, 6, and mark off a corresponding number on the curve for the pattern; the length from A' to 6 (Fig. 77) will then equal one-fourth the circumference of the base of the cone. Repeat this distance (A' 6) at B', C', D', and so make the curve of the pattern equal in length to the circumference of the base of the cone. Join A' and D' to the centre O. Now take the distance o' a' (Fig. 76) as radius, and using O (Fig. 77) as centre, describe the inner arc a d to complete the pattern. Allowances for wiring, grooving, etc., when making a conical tube of this kind are shown in Fig. 77.

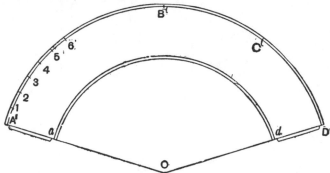

Fig. 77.—Second Method of Setting Out Frustum of Right Cone.

To determine the development and section of a cylindrical elbow. PROBLEM 38.—Fig. 78 shows the half-plan and elevation of a cylinder, A B C D, to be cut so that when the parts are joined a double right-angled elbow may be formed. The section must be made at half that angle with the axis. Thus, if a pipe is to follow two walls which meet at an angle of 120°, each part must be cut at 60°. Therefore, in the present instance, draw the section lines E F and G H at 45° to the axis.

To develop the cylinder, divide the half-plan into any number of equal parts, as shown at A, b, c, d, e, f, D. Draw a horizontal line, and erect on it a perpendicular at A' (Fig. 79). On each side of A' set off the lengths to b', c', d', e', f', and D', and b'', c'' d'', e'', f'', and D'', taken from Fig. 78. At D' and D'' erect perpendiculars, and from B (Fig. 78) project a horizontal so as to form the rectangle D' B'' B''' D', which is then the development of the entire cylinder. To trace on this development the lines in which the metal is to be cut so that the three parts may be accurately formed without any waste, from b c d e f in Fig. 78 draw per-

pendiculars cutting the section line E F at the points shown. From
the points b', c', d', e', and f', in Fig. 79, erect perpendiculars, and

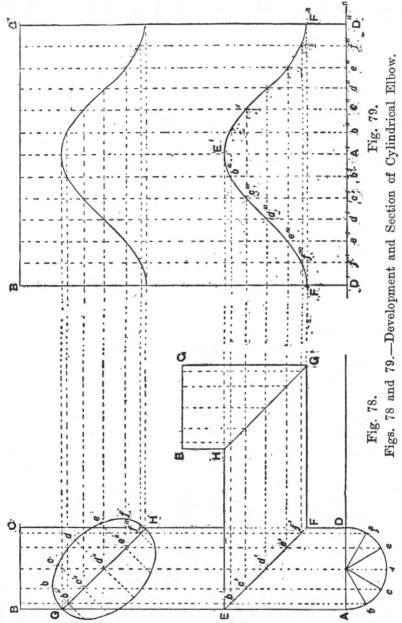

Fig. 79.

Fig. 78.

Figs. 78 and 79.—Development and Section of Cylindrical Elbow.

from the intersections b', c', d', e', f', E, and F, in Fig. 78, draw
horizontal lines cutting the perpendiculars in Fig. 79 in F', E', F'',

b''', c''', d''', e''', f''', etc.   The line drawn through these points will be the curve required.   The upper curve is obtained in precisely the same manner, the horizontals being drawn from the points in the line G H, of Fig. 78.

To find the true section on either of the two lines, draw lines through the points b'', c'', d'', e'', and f'', at right angles to G H (Fig. 78).   On each side of G H set off on these lines lengths equal to those drawn from b, c, d, e, f, to A D in the half-plan, below. Join these points, and the ellipse thus drawn will be the true section.

To draw the projections and development of two cylinders inter-secting at right angles.   PROBLEM 39.—In Fig. 80 the circle A B represents the plan of the larger, and the rectangle D D′ E′ E that of the smaller cylinder.   From this figure project the cross that forms the elevation, drawing perpendiculars from A B to be terminated at the length above X Y corresponding with the height of the larger cylinder.   Next draw the smaller cylinder which crosses the larger one horizontally.

The line C″ A B G″, which is the top of the smaller cylinder in the elevation, is the middle line C C′ in the plan, and the line D E, which is the prominent line of the cylinder in the plan, is repre-sented by D″ E″, the middle line in the elevation.

From C′ in the plan, with radius C′ E, describe a semicircle, which represents half the circular plane of the end of the cylinder.   This plane may be supposed to stand upright on the line E E′, at right angles to the plan.   Divide the semicircle into any number of equal parts, and from these divisions draw lines meeting E E′ at right angles in F, G, H, and J.   Set off the lengths of these perpendiculars on each side of the line D″ E″ in the eleva-tion, so that E″ F′ and E″ F″ equal F f or J j, and E″ G′ and E″ G″ equal G g or H h, and draw lines from these points across the ele-vation of the smaller cylinder.   Draw similar lines parallel to C C′ from the corresponding points in the plan, and from the points A and B (in the plan), h', j', and e draw perpendiculars to meet the horizontals in the elevation.   The intersections B, g', f', e'', h'', j'', and b will give the points through which the curve of penetration is to be drawn.   The left-hand curve A a can be drawn in a similar manner.

In developing the surfaces of the larger cylinder, it must be borne in mind that the form of the aperture through which the smaller cylinder is to pass will not be a circle when laid out flat.

Develop the cylinder B′ B″ (Fig. 81) as before described in Problem 38, pp. 66-68. Draw a centre line at A′ representing A

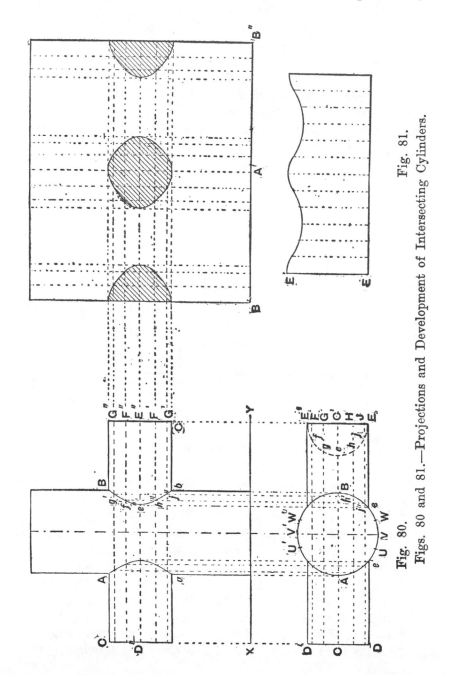

Fig. 81.

Fig. 80.

Figs. 80 and 81.—Projections and Development of Intersecting Cylinders.

in the plan and on each side set off lengths as shown, measuring round the circle in Fig. 80, and erect perpendiculars. Then the heights of the points in the elevation (Fig. 80), when marked off on these perpendiculars, will give the points through which the form of the apertures may be traced.

As this development meets at the middle of one aperture, half of the form must be drawn at B′ and half at B″. Also, since the difference between the chord from *e* to *e′* (Fig. 80) and the curve is considerable, the distance should be again divided into a number of parts at U, V, W, U′, V′, and W′, and set off on B′ B″, on Fig, 81, as shown. By this means the risk of inaccuracy may be considerably lessened.

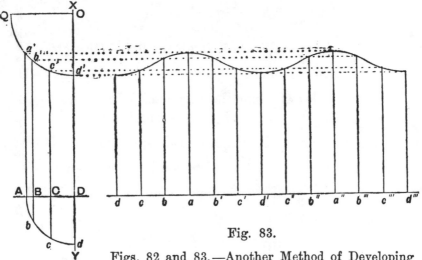

Fig. 83.

Figs. 82 and 83.—Another Method of Developing
Fig. 82.   Intersecting Cylinders.

To develop the form of one of the ends of the penetrating or smaller cylinder, draw a horizontal line, and erect a perpendicular E E′ (Fig. 81). On each side of this point set off the distances into which the end of the smaller cylinder is divided, and from these points erect perpendiculars. On these, set off the lengths of the lines between E E′ and the plan of the larger cylinder, namely, E *e*, J *j′*, H *h′*, etc. (Fig. 80). The curve uniting the extremities of these perpendiculars will give the form in which the metal must be cut.

Another Method.—A shorter method of developing intersecting cylinders than that described above is the following :—With any point in the X Y as centre, and with radius equal to that of the vertical pipe, describe the quarter circle O Q d' (Fig. 82). Make d' D equal to the distance the horizontal cylinder stands out from the vertical one. Use D as centre, and with the radius of the horizontal cylinder describe the quarter circle D A d. Divide this curve into any convenient number of equal parts, as at A, b, c, and d, and from these points draw lines parallel to X Y to cut the other quarter circle at a', b', and c'. Join A D and produce the line d d''', and along it mark four times as many divisions as there are in the smaller quarter circle, as d, c, b, a, etc., to d''' (see pattern, Fig. 83). On perpendiculars erected at these points mark

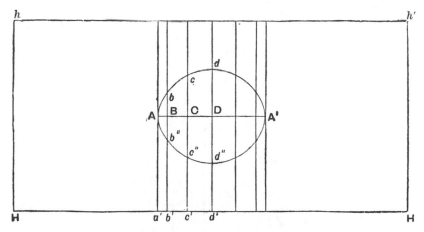

Fig. 84.—Intersection of Two Cylinders.

off the lengths shown by the projection lines, transfer these lengths to the verticals on Fig. 83 with corresponding letters, and through the points thus found draw an unbroken curve to complete the pattern for the horizontal cylinder.

For the vertical cylinder, draw a rectangle H h h' H$'$ (Fig. 84) as high as the cylinder and equal in length to its circumference. Draw a centre line at d', and on either side of d' mark the distance d' c' (Fig. 82). Next transfer the distance c' b' and b' a' (Fig. 82) to Fig. 84; in the same way, and at the points thus found, draw lines perpendicular to H H$'$. Mark D the centre of the horizontal cylinder on d' (Fig. 84), and through it draw A A$'$ parallel to H H$'$. Now mark the distance D d (Fig. 82) above and below D on the line d' as d d'', and similarly mark the two lengths corresponding to c c'' and to b b'' (Fig. 84) from C c and B b

(Fig. 82). The curve through the points thus found shows the true shape of the intersection.

Patterns for a Cone Penetrating a Cylinder. PROBLEM 40.—To set out the patterns for a cone penetrating a cylinder, with the

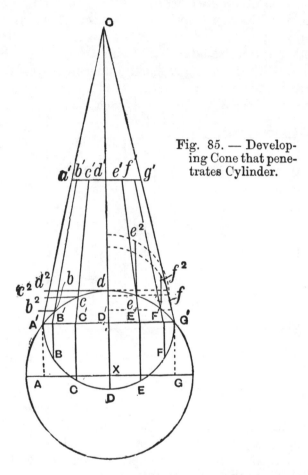

Fig. 85. — Developing Cone that penetrates Cylinder.

axes at **right** angles to and intersecting each other, first draw the plan of the cylinder when standing on its base horizontally ; then from the centre x (Fig. 85) draw a line at right angles to the centre line, and on each side of x mark the radius of the base of the cone as indicated by A G. Draw lines from A and G at right angles to the centre line to join the plan of the cylinder at A' G', and join these last points by a straight line, which will be the base of the cone. With D' as centre and D' A' as radius, draw the semicircle A' D G'. Next from *d* mark off the height of the smaller end of the cone, as d', and through this point draw a line at right angles to o d', the axis of the cone. Mark off the radius of the small end of the cone as d' a', d' g', then join a' a' and g' g' and produce the lines until they intersect at o; this will give a complete plan of a cone containing the given frustum. Divide the semicircle at the base of the cone into any convenient number of equal parts, and from each division point B, C, D, E, F, draw projectors at right angles to the base of the cone to join the base at B', C', D', E', F', and join these points by straight lines to the apex

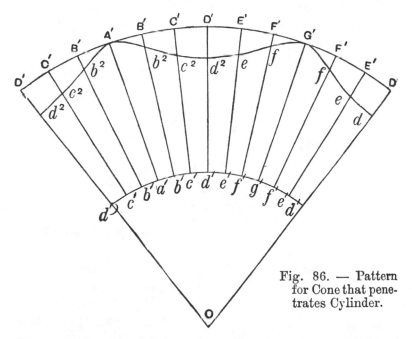

Fig. 86. — Pattern for Cone that penetrates Cylinder.

o. The points of intersection of the lines on the cone and on the side of the cylinder will be where these lines pass through the plan of the cylinder at b, c, d, e, f. To obtain the true lengths of the stripes where they join the cylinder, draw lines parallel to the base of the cone from b, c, and d to cut the true slant a' a'. Use the full slant o a' as radius for drawing the pattern, and, taking any point as centre (o, Fig. 86), draw an arc of a circle. Take one of the divisions of the base of the cone as radius, and mark off upon the arc a number of divisions equal to those in a complete circumference of the base of the cone; in this case they will be twelve, as shown at D', C', B', A', B', C', D', E', F', G', F', E', D' (Fig. 86). With o a' (Fig. 85) as radius, draw the arc d' d' (Fig. 86) to form the curve for the smaller end of the cone, and join the division points D' C', etc., to the centre O. Then, assuming that the seam is to occur at the line D (Fig. 85), take the true length on the slant of the cone from the apex to the point of penetration—that is, from d^2 to O—and transfer the length to the stripes d' D' on to the pattern, as O d^2 (Fig. 86). Transfer O c^2 and O b^2 to their respective stripes, and to the stripes in corresponding positions on the opposite side of the pattern ; draw a curve through the points found, d^2, c^2, b^2, etc., and this curve will form the part of the cone to fit the cylinder. To draw the shape of the hole in the cylinder, for use as a pattern to mark the hole in the required position, commence by transferring the divisions around the plan of the cylinder A' b c d e f G' (Fig. 85) to a straight line A' G' (Fig. 87). Through each division point draw lines at right angles

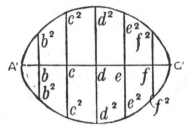

Fig. 87.—Shape of Hole in Cylinder penetrated by Cone.

to and above and below the line first drawn. Make d d^2 (Fig. 87) equal to d d^2 (Fig. 85). Now draw lines parallel to the base of the cone to contain the points e and f (Fig. 85) and touching the axis and the slant side of the cone. Then using the ends of the lines on the axis as alternate centres, and with a radius to the end of the lines on the slant, draw the two dotted quarter circles shown in Fig. 85. From e draw a perpendicular line to cut the quarter circle at e^2, and transfer this length e e^2 to the lines e e^2, c c^2 (Fig. 87), marking the distance from the centre line A' G' above and below in each case. Erect a perpendicular from f to f^2 (Fig. 85), and transfer this to f f^2, b b^2 (Fig. 87), as with the previous stripe. Draw a curve through A' b^2 c^2 d^2 e^2 f^2 G', and this will be the shape of the hole for marking in the required position on the cylinder. On the cone pattern, all allowances for seams, flanges, etc., will need to be drawn outside the lines already drawn. Fig. 85 shows a side elevation of cone and cylinder, Fig. 86 shows development of cone, whilst Fig. 87 is a plan of intersection of cone and cylinder.

To determine the developments of a cone and cylinder that meet obliquely, the whole of the section plane being common to both. PROBLEM 41.—First draw plan and elevation of the cylinder in

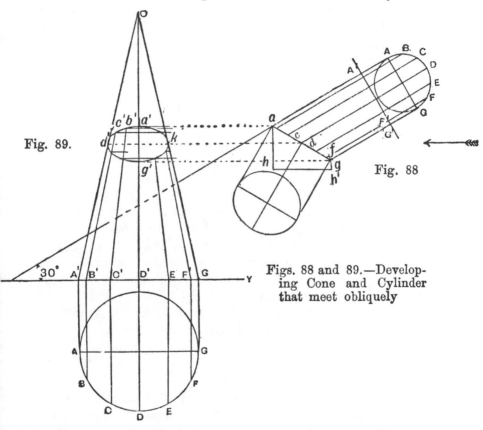

Fig. 89.

Fig. 88

Figs. 88 and 89.—Developing Cone and Cylinder that meet obliquely

position, with its sides making the required angle (say 30°) with the ground line, as A' *a, g* G' (Fig. 88). Make A' *a* equal to the greatest length of the cylinder, then drop a vertical from *a*, and set off a line at right angles to it, as *h h'*. Make *h h'* equal to the diameter of the cylinder, and through the point *h'* draw a line parallel to *a h* to intersect the underside of the cylinder at *g*; join *a g* for the mitre line. The true section is the ellipse shown in Fig. 88, the minor axis of which is equal to the diameter of the cylinder. Next construct an elevation of the cone which will contain the ellipse of intersection and which will also have the plane containing the ellipse inclined at the same angle to the ground as the inclina-tion of the mitre line on the cylinder. If the diameter of the base of the cone and the greatest height are also given, then a view of the section of the cylinder could be drawn, looking from the direction indicated by the arrow (Fig. 88), and this ellipse could be used as the commencement of the elevation of the cone. To draw the elevation of a cone containing the given elliptic section of the cylinder, first draw the projectors joining Figs. 88 and 89, at *a, d, g,* etc. (Fig. 88), and then erect a perpendicular

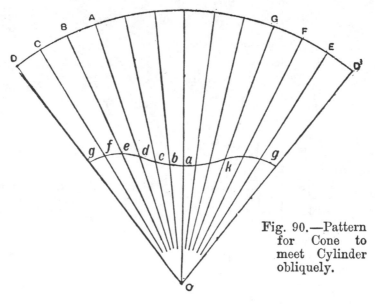

Fig. 90.—Pattern for Cone to meet Cylinder obliquely.

D′ O from the ground line to the projectors last drawn. This line may be assumed to represent the axis of the cone. On each side of the axis mark half the distance required for the diameter of the base of the cone A′ G′, and then mark half the diameter of the cylinder on each side of the axis of the cone along the projector drawn from *d* (Fig. 88), as *d′ k′* (Fig. 89). The distance between *a′* and D′ should equal the greatest height of cone when cut. Now draw the ellipse shown on the elevation of the cone. Draw tangents to the ellipse to join A′ and G′, produce them to intersect at O, and divide the plan of the cone into any suitable number of equal parts. From the division points A, B, C, D, E, F, and G erect perpendiculars to cut the ground line X Y at A′, B′, C′, D′, E′, F′, and G′, and connect each of these points by a straight line with the apex of the cone. The intersection of these lines with the ellipse indicates the perpendicular height above the ground of the points a', b', c', d', etc., on the edge of the ellipse. To find the true length from the ground to where each line joins the ellipse, from the points a', c', d', g', etc., draw lines parallel to the base of the cone to cut g' o in the true length required.

Draw the pattern of the complete cone (Fig. 90) as described in Problem 36, p. 61. Connect each of the division points between D and D' by a line with the centre o ; these lines show the true length of the stripes in Fig. 89. Then with o as centre, take the lengths to a', b', c', d', etc., on the side of the cone (Fig 89), and transfer these to the stripes with corresponding letters on the

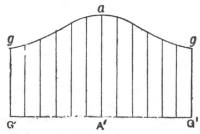

Fig. 91.—Pattern for Cylinder to meet Cone Obliquely.

pattern (Fig. 90). Through the points thus found draw a curve for the top part of the cone.

The pattern for the cylinder can be obtained by setting off along a straight line a number of equal divisions corresponding to those in the circumference of the base of the cylinder as g' g' (Fig. 91). From the division point erect perpendiculars, and mark off lengths on these equal to those on the stripes with corresponding letters in Fig. 88. Commencing with the length g' g (Fig. 88), mark this off on each end stripe of the pattern (Fig. 91) ; then take the length f' f (Fig. 88) and transfer to the second and last but one stripes on the pattern, and continue until all the lengths have been transferred, the lengths in each case being measured from the end of the cylinder to the mitre line ; draw a curve through the points thus obtained to complete the pattern All allowances for seams, flanges, etc., must be added to the pattern where required.

Setting out patterns for oblique cones. PROBLEM 42.—To mark out patterns for three oblique cones, as K, L, M (Fig. 92), the method of working would be the same for each section, therefore only the pattern for the section marked K is worked. On the ground line mark the diameter of the base of the cone, and set off from A a line at the required inclination. At the requisite height, draw the line $a^1 g$ parallel to the ground line, and of a length equal to the diameter of the cylinder. Produce the lines A a^1 and H g until they intersect at o; the figure formed will be an elevation of an oblique cone containing the given section. Now draw the elevation of the cones L, M by the same method. Where the longest generating line of the cone L passes through the shortest generating line of the cone K will give the top point (g^1) on the first section. Join g^1 to o^2, the centre of the base. Find the highest point on the section joining cones L and M, g^2, and also join this point to o^2; then $g^1 o^2$, $g^2 o^2$ will be section lines on the elevation where the three cones are joined. Draw the semicircle $a^1 d g$, and divide it into any convenient number of equal parts, b, c, d, e, and f; draw a perpendicular from o to join $a^1 g$ at o^1; use o^1 as centre, and, with radius to each division point, swing round arcs of circles to join $a^1 g$. Join o with the ground-line A H by lines passing through the points b^1, c^1, d^1, e^1, f^1; then these lines, which need not necessarily be drawn above the line $a^1 g$, would be the true slants or generating lines for transferring to the pattern; they cut the line A H at the points B, C, D, and E. The line from f^1 is not shown. Draw perpendiculars from the division points e, f to cut $a^1 g$, and through the apex of the cone draw lines from the points found down to the section line $g^1 o^2$. These lines represent the position of the generating lines on the elevation before being swung back to obtain their true length, and where these elevation lines join the section line at the points e^2, f^2 would be the points where the stripes were cut. To find the true length of these stripes, draw lines parallel to the base of the cone from the points e^2 and f^2, until they intersect the generating lines with corresponding letters at e^3, f^3. To work the pattern for the cone K, draw a straight line A $a^1 o$ (Fig. 93) and mark from o the length $o a^1$ transferred from Fig. 92. Now take the lengths o to $b^1, c^1, d^1, e^1, f^1, g$ (Fig. 92) as radius, and, using o (Fig. 93) as centre, draw a series of arcs of circles as shown. Take the division $a^1 b$ (Fig. 92) as radius, and, using a^1 (Fig. 93) as centre, cut the first arc drawn at $b^1 b^1$; with the same division lengths as radius, and using $b^1 b^1$ as centres, cut the second arc at $c^1 c^1$, and step down to each arc until the remaining points d^1, e^1, f^1, g, are obtained; draw a curve through the points found, and this curve

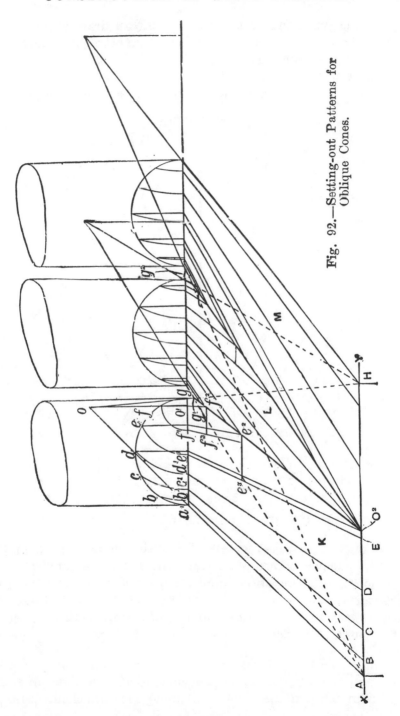

Fig. 92.—Setting-out Patterns for Oblique Cones.

will be the small end of the pattern. Now draw straight lines from o through each division point, then take the length o to A B C D (Fig. 92) and mark them from o (Fig. 93) on the stripes with corresponding letters. Then take the lengths o e^3, $o f^3$, and o g^1 (Fig. 92), and transfer these to the stripes with corresponding

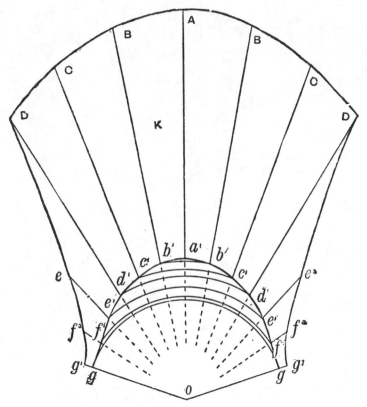

Fig. 93.—Pattern for Oblique Cones.

letters on the pattern (Fig. 93). Draw the curve A B C D and D $e^3 f^3 g^1$, as shown, to complete the pattern for the cone K. The elevational and generating lines necessary for working the patterns for L and M are shown by Fig. 92, and from these the patterns may be obtained by adopting the same method of working as for the first cone.

CHAPTER IV.

TOOLS AND APPLIANCES USED IN METAL PLATE WORK.

In this chapter mention will be made of the more important of the tools and appliances called into requisition by the metal plate worker. Detailed description of each tool need not be given, as, by the aid of the illustration, the use of the tool may in most cases be inferred. Where this is not possible, particulars of the manner in which the tool is used will be included in the

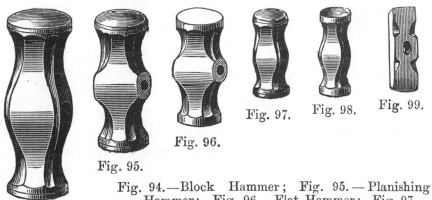

Fig. 97.   Fig. 98.   Fig. 99.

Fig. 96.

Fig. 95.

Fig. 94.—Block Hammer; Fig. 95.—Planishing Hammer; Fig. 96.—Flat Hammer; Fig. 97.—Convex Hammer; Fig. 98.—Concave Hammer; Fig. 99.—Pane Hammer.

Fig. 94.

descriptions of the practical processes involved in shaping metal plate, to be given in Chapter VII.

A commencement will be made with those tools of a simple character, and of these the hammers naturally take first place.

A large block hammer is illustrated by Fig. 94; a planishing hammer, by Fig. 95; a flat hammer, by Fig. 96; a convex hammer, by Fig. 97; a concave hammer, by Fig. 98; a pane hammer, by Fig. 99; a box hammer, by Fig. 100; a square-faced hammer, by Fig. 101; a riveting hammer, by Fig. 102; a smoothing hammer, by Fig. 103; and a hollowing hammer, by Fig. 104. A mallet, Fig. 105, completes the list of percussive tools: this should be of boxwood, and from 2 in. to 3 in. in

F

diameter. One, $2\frac{1}{4}$ in. in diameter, is suitable for light work; for heavier work, one $2\frac{3}{4}$ in. in diameter is used.

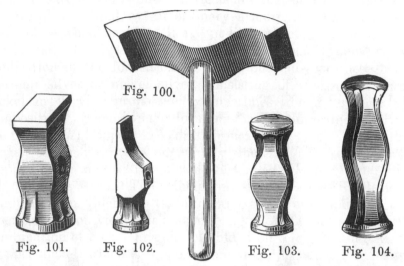

Fig. 100.

Fig. 101.   Fig. 102.   Fig. 103.   Fig. 104.

Fig. 100. — Box Hammer; Fig. 101. — Square-faced Hammer; Fig. 102.—Riveting Hammer; Fig. 103.—Smoothing Hammer; Fig. 104.—Hollowing Hammer.

Sheet metal is shaped, principally, by being bent over anvils of peculiar forms known as stakes. These fit into holes cut in the bench, and are of many kinds, as the following list will show:

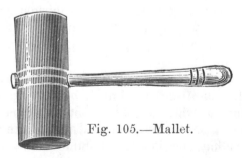

Fig. 105.—Mallet.

Fig. 106 shows the tinman's anvil; it is steel-faced, highly polished, and nearly flat. The anvil is usually fixed in a block, but sometimes in a large hole cut for it in the bench. On this tool is done the planishing of plain surfaces in tin, brass, or copper. Fig. 107 shows the anvil stake—a similar tool, but smaller. Fig. 108 is a round bottom stake, of use in riveting patches on the bottoms of pans. Two or three sizes are required.

Fig. 109 is a convex stake, used in forming the tops of pepper or flour boxes. Fig. 110 is a creasing stake, or crease iron, as

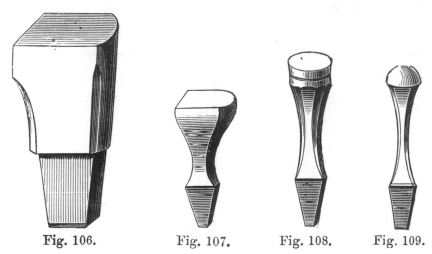

Fig. 106.   Fig. 107.   Fig. 108.   Fig. 109.

Fig. 106.—Anvil; Fig. 107.—Anvil Stake; Fig. 108.—Round Stake; Fig. 109.—Convex Stake.

it is usually called : its grooved part is for sinking wire, or turning stays on a length of rod, and its flat part can be used, in the

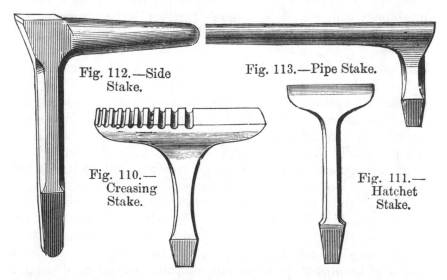

Fig. 112.—Side Stake.

Fig. 113.—Pipe Stake.

Fig. 110.— Creasing Stake.

Fig. 111.— Hatchet Stake.

absence of a jenny (see p. 89), for paning down, for wiring, and for various other purposes. The hatchet stake, Fig. 111, is used for edging up tin plate, etc., where there is no folding machine, for folding sheet iron and sheet zinc, and for preparing the bottoms of articles that have to be "knocked up" or "closed" in a machine. On the side stake, Fig. 112, is done most of the seaming. The pipe stake, Fig. 113, is a somewhat similar tool, but

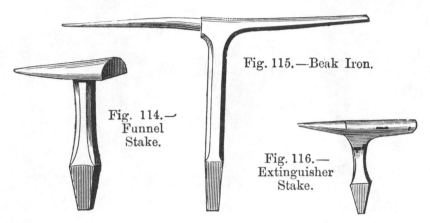

Fig. 115.—Beak Iron.

Fig. 114.—Funnel Stake.

Fig. 116.—Extinguisher Stake.

shorter in the stem and longer in the arm; it has a rounded end, which is shortened in Fig. 113. It is used for seaming sheet-iron stove pipe and for knocking up. Fig. 114 shows a funnel stake, used for shaping funnels and for grooving or

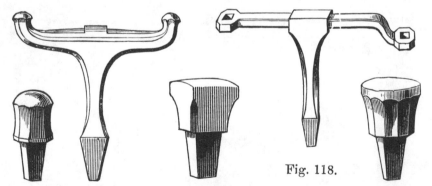

Fig. 119.   Fig. 117.   Fig. 120.   Fig. 121.

Fig. 118.

Fig. 117.—Saucepan Belly Stake; Fig. 118.—Horse; Figs. 119—121.— Horse-heads.

seaming them. Fig. 115 is a beak iron; two or three of these are required to turn the various sizes of saucepan handles, water-pot spouts, etc. Fig. 116 shows an extinguisher stake, somewhat resembling a beak iron, but much smaller. Fig. 117 is a saucepan belly stake, used in shaping bellied saucepans. Fig. 118 shows the tinman's horse, having a hole at both of its ends to receive the horse-heads, Figs. 119, 120, and 121. The half-moon stake, Fig. 122, is employed, chiefly, in turning up the bottoms of vessels.

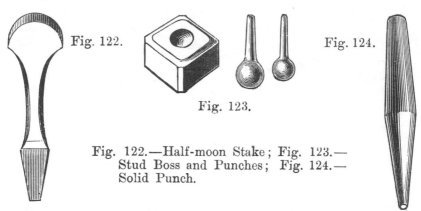

Fig. 122.   Fig. 123.   Fig. 124.

Fig. 122.—Half-moon Stake; Fig. 123.—
Stud Boss and Punches; Fig. 124.—
Solid Punch.

The tools used in forming the half-spherical studs that are soldered to the bottoms of water-cans, etc., may be mentioned briefly here. The studs may be punched out with a large hollow punch on a lead piece; this is a block of lead about $1\frac{1}{2}$ in. thick,

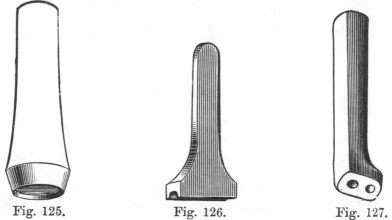

Fig. 125.   Fig. 126.   Fig. 127.

Fig. 125.—Hollow Punch; Fig. 126.—Groove Punch or Groover;
Fig. 127.—Rivet Set.

and from 8 in. to 12 in. square; they are then hollowed with a small hollowing hammer, called a stud hammer, in a hollow made in the lead piece, or with a stud boss and punch, Fig. 123. Figs. 124 and 125 show solid and hollow punches. The first kind range from $\frac{1}{16}$ in. to $\frac{7}{16}$ in., in about ten sizes, and the second kind from $\frac{3}{8}$ in. to $2\frac{1}{2}$ in. Fig. 126 shows a groove punch, or groover, as it is generally named : it is used in laying seams together. Fig. 127 is a rivet set used in drawing through rivets (see p. 128)

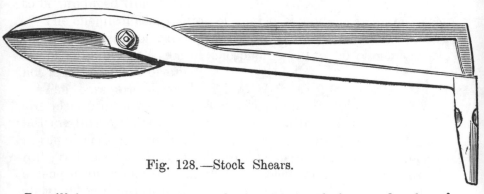

Fig. 128.—Stock Shears.

It will be necessary to have three or four of these only, though there are about sixteen sizes made.

Sheet metal is cut to pattern as required by means of shears.

Fig. 129.—Hand or Scotch Shears.

These may be had in a variety of shapes, but those that are really necessary are (*a*) stock shears, Fig. 128, for cutting out new work in large quantities, and (*b*) hand or Scotch shears, Fig. 129, for

Fig. 130.—Bent Snips.

Fig. 131.—Straight Snips.

more general use on lighter material. In addition to these, bent snips, Fig. 130, and straight snips, Fig. 131, will be required for small work, principally connected with repairs.

Fig. 132 shows the square for marking out, squaring-up sheet, etc. It is divided along its edges and figured on both sides.

It is made in five sizes, ranging from 18 in. × 12 in. to 24 in. × 18 in. The 24 in. × 12 in., known as the "two-foot square," is the one mostly used.

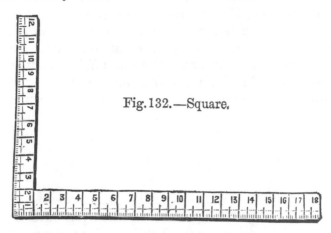

Fig. 132.—Square.

A small assortment of cold chisels should be obtained, and this should include the flat chisel, Fig. 133, the cross-cut chisel,

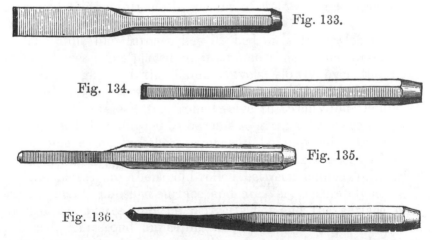

Fig. 133.

Fig. 134.

Fig. 135.

Fig. 136.

Fig. 133.—Flat Chisel; Fig. 134.—Cross-cut Chisel; Fig. 135.—
Foal's-foot Chisel; Fig. 136.—Diamond-point Chisel.

Fig. 134, the foal's-foot chisel, Fig. 135, and the diamond-point chisel, Fig. 136. The list of small hand tools in every-day use may conclude with mention of round-nosed pliers, Fig. 137, and tinmen's pliers, Fig. 138.

The hand tools must be arranged in the workshop conveniently near the bench : the heavy stakes can be kept on the floor, whilst the lighter ones may be hung on the wall, each between two stout nails. Punches, rivet sets, groovers, and small tools may be in trays at the back of the bench and in front of the worker. Keep all bright tools and hammers well greased when not in use, and spirits of salts and sal-ammoniac must be kept as far away from them as is convenient.

The tools and appliances used in soldering form a part of the

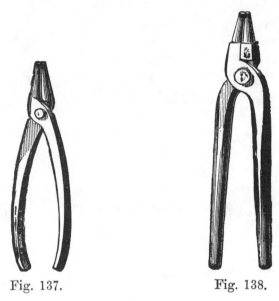

Fig. 137.   Fig. 138.

Figs. 137 and 138.—Pliers.

metal plate worker's tool outfit of course ; these, however, are dealt with fully in Chapter V., which is ᐧ devoted exclusively to the methods of forming hard and soft soldered joints and to the tools and materials necessary for such work.

The principal hand tools having been mentioned, it now remains to give some particulars of the heavier appliances and machines that have a place in a well-appointed metal plate workshop. The mention of these machines must not be taken by the reader to imply that good work cannot be done without their aid. As a matter of fact, it is only large shops and factories that possess all those machines described below.

The burring machine or jenny, Fig. 139, is used to "edge"

bottoms and bodies, to "crease" and edge covers and funnels, close tin plate round wires, etc. Its shank is so shaped that it fits into a hole cut in the bench, or the machine may be fitted into standards, such as Figs. 140 and 141, and these can then be clamped anywhere on the edge of the bench.

In the burring machine illustrated, the creasing wheels are screwed on the spindles and riveted, thus allowing the work to be put through backwards or forwards without fear of the wheel screwing off the spindle, as may occur with heads that are

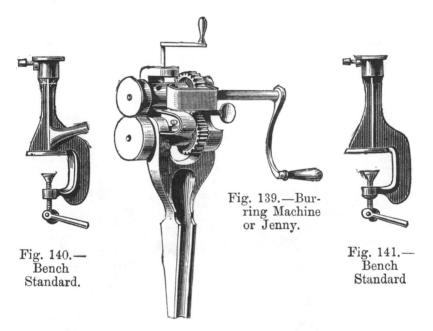

Fig. 139.—Burring Machine or Jenny.

Fig. 140.—Bench Standard.

Fig. 141.—Bench Standard

screwed to the spindle only. The machines are made in four weights—12 lb. to 53 lb.—the smallest having a top creasing wheel 1½ in. diameter, the largest having one of 3½ in. diameter.

For shaping sheet metal into cylinders, bending rollers are employed. Before their introduction the work had to be turned on a tool called a former, Fig. 142. Formers were made in various sizes, and good work could be done with them, but as a labour-saving device the bending rollers have superseded them. Fig. 143 shows a set of tinman's rollers, particularly suited to rolling small tubes, canister bodies, etc. It consists of cast-iron standards supporting three rollers, two being in front, one over the other, and one at the back. At the right-hand end of the two front rollers are two toothed wheels, which communicate the motion.   The top roller works in bearings that

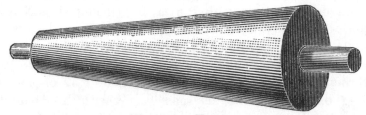

Fig. 142.—Former.

are lifted or depressed by means of screws having cranked handles as shown.   The top roller regulates the pressure, but

Fig. 143.—Tube Bending Rollers.

the size of the tube being rolled depends principally on the position of the back roller.   The smaller the tube, the lower it is let down ; and the larger the tube, the higher is the roller brought up.

In the type of machine shown, the roller on which the tube is formed is easily lifted out of its bearings, to allow very small tubes to be removed without injury. Other types of bending machines are made, but they differ only in detail and not in principle from the one illustrated by Fig. 143.

Fig. 144 shows a machine for turning or folding the edges

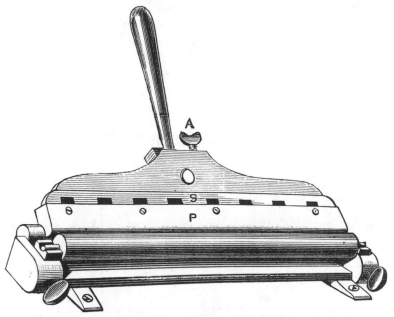

Fig. 144.—Folding Machine.

of tin goods that have to be joined by grooving. This folding machine is held down to the bench by screws passed through four lugs. The pieces of sheet metal to be folded are slipped over the front roller under the steel plate, P ; the distance they are to be bent is regulated by the notched brass slide, S, which is moved by turning the regulating screw, A. With the front roller high, a sharp fold is obtained ; when it is low, the fold is more rounded. These machines are made in about seven sizes, the smallest being 18 in. long and weighing 34 lbs., and the largest being 48 in. long and weighing a little more than 2 cwt. No. 1½ is the most useful size for most ordinary work. It is about 20 in. long.

Fig. 145 shows a bottom-closing or "knocking-up" machine. It is used for turning up the bottoms of saucepans, water-pots,

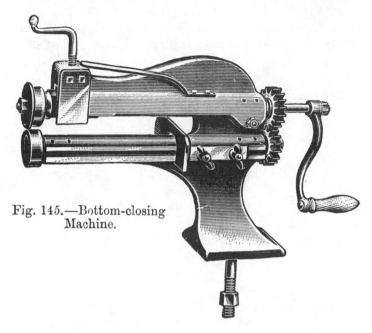

Fig. 145.—Bottom-closing Machine.

and similar vessels. When the bottom seam has been paned and partially bent up, this machine closes the edges of the

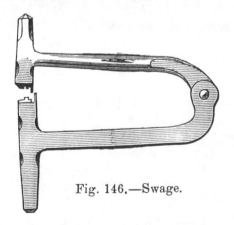

Fig. 146.—Swage.

bottom against the sides. With this machine, also, the bottoms of light canisters can be crimped on ; solder is not necessary then.

Fig. 146 shows one form of swage. It is used for making the beading that forms the seat of the kettle cover ; and it is fitted to receive various heads. The colander swage and the three-thread swage have the same principle of construction, differing merely in the shape of the dies.

The paning down machine, Fig. 147, closes the bottoms of articles after they have been edged up in the jenny; or the bottoms may be tapped round with a light hammer and run

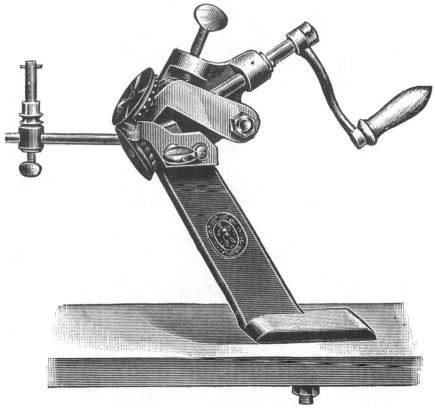

Fig. 147.—Paning Down Machine.

round in this machine, once to close the edge, and then once more to bend the edge of the bottom up a little, ready for the mallet or bottom-closing machine.

Fig. 148 shows a circle cutter for tin plate; this is bolted to the bench for use. The sheet of metal to be cut has the circle described on it by means of a pair of compasses, and it is then placed on the machine, the screw A being placed on the centre mark. The bow D is drawn along the frame of the machine till the two cutters are just on the circular line required to be cut; the screw B is then tightened down, the handle turned, and the circle cut. Uniformity in size and truth of circle is secured by the use of this machine. The smallest machine of the type illustrated by Fig. 148 will cut circles from $2\frac{1}{2}$ in. to 14 in. diameter; the largest will cut circles from $4\frac{1}{2}$ in. to 18 in. diameter. Heavier machines than the one shown by the illustration are made; their construction is on a similar principle, though they differ in detail.

As a conclusion to this chapter on tools and appliances, something must be said concerning the metal plate worker's bench. It should be made of good sound beech or other tough, hard wood. Soft woods—such as deal or pine—will not stand the pulling and straining occasioned by very heavy work. In thickness it should be not less than 3 in. at the front half, in which are cut the holes or mortises for the stake tools, on which all the hammering, etc., is done; the back half may be much less, say 1 in. or $1\frac{1}{4}$ in. thick. It should be from 2 ft. to 2 ft. 6 in. wide, and as long as the workshop will allow; a good average height is 30 in. A tall man will require it 1 in. higher, a short man, 1 in. lower.

A short bench will require to be supported at the ends only; but if over 8 ft. long, it will want support in the centre. It must be fixed very firmly, or it will soon be loosened when using the heavy stakes and tools. A reliable method of fixing the bench is to have stout posts fixed to the floor, with pieces running from the posts to the wall, into which they are let and fixed; the bench is laid on these, and screwed or bolted down. A short return piece is very useful on the right-hand end of the bench to support the folding machine and tools. Some square holes have to be cut in the bench to receive the stakes, etc.; it is desirable that the holes be few. In cutting out the holes, first mark them out square on the bench not nearer to the edge than $1\frac{1}{2}$ in., and not farther away than 2 in. Let the holes be 6 in. apart, and do not have more than four; find the centre by drawing diagonal lines from corner to corner, and bore a hole with a bit a little larger than the square is to be, afterwards cutting out the corners with a joiner's chisel. Cut the first hole to the size of the foot of the largest stake but one and the hole will then do for, perhaps, three different stakes. A larger hole should be cut, and then one for the smaller stakes, and one for the stock shears. Sometimes the holes are countersunk, and plates of iron, having square holes cut through their

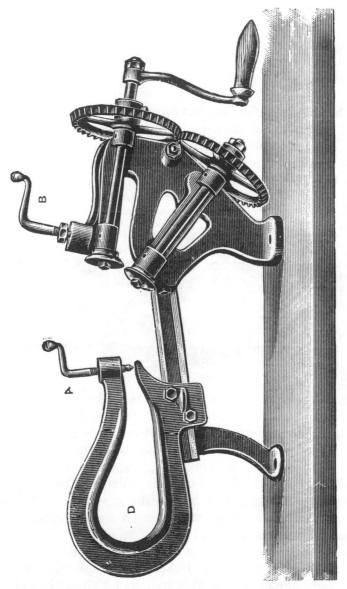

Fig. 148.—Circle Cutting Machine.

centres, are let in to prevent the tools wearing off the edges
of the wooden bench.

CHAPTER V.

SOLDERING AND BRAZING.

SOLDERING may be defined as the uniting of two metals by means of a more fusible metal or metallic alloy ; this easily fused metal or solder, as it is termed, is usually applied in metal plate work with a heated copper bit, mis-called a soldering iron, various fluxes being used to facilitate the melting and flowing of the solder and to assist it to adhere to the two surfaces to be joined.

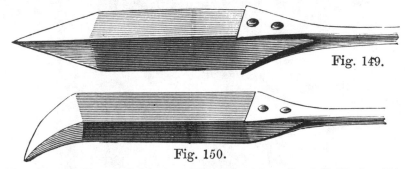

Fig. 149.

Fig. 150.

Fig. 149.—Ordinary Soldering Bit; Fig. 150.—Bent Soldering Bit.

It may be as well to give some particulars of the requisite tools and materials before describing the practical soldering processes.

The soldering bits differ in size and shape, according to the work to be done. Fig. 149 is the ordinary pointed soldering bit used for general work ; Fig. 150 shows a lighter tool, having a bent point. The bottoming bit, Fig. 151, is used for soldering round the bottoms of saucepans and similar vessels. A hatchet bit is illustrated by Fig. 152. Soldering bits should have from 4 in. to 5 in. of copper, in addition to that which is riveted in the shank, as in constant usage the length soon diminishes by filing and drawing out. A copper bit that has a long shank fatigues the arm quickly, not only by the weight of the tool, but by the cramped position into which it throws the arm. For general use

the soldering bit should be about 16 in. long from point to
extremity of handle. The latter should be made so as to afford
a firm grasp and balance the copper. Good handles are turned
from sound beech, and are about 5 in. long and $1\frac{1}{8}$ in. to $1\frac{1}{4}$ in. in
diameter. A groove is turned in the handle to receive a binding
of copper wire instead of a ferrule. A hole, the size of the round
shank, should be bored about three-fourths of the way up the
handle ; the remainder should be bored smaller for the pointed
end of the shank to come through about $\frac{1}{4}$ in., this end being either
bent and clenched into the end of the handle or riveted with a
small burr or washer. For heating the copper bit some form

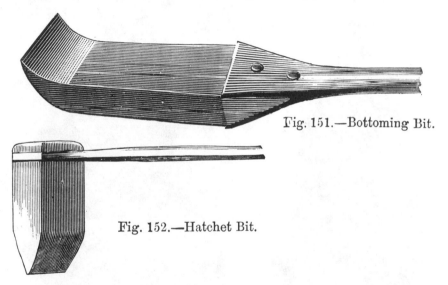

Fig. 151.—Bottoming Bit.

Fig. 152.—Hatchet Bit.

of stove will be required. There are several stoves made specially
for the purpose. Fig. 153 shows a common form of fire-pot mostly
used for outdoor work ; a simple stove on the lines of this may be
made easily by the metal plate worker himself. Fig. 154 shows a
good form for indoor use. The top part lifts off; the front and
outside grating are in one piece, and are easy of removal when it
is required to clear out the ashes that drop through from the top
part ; the whole stands in a cast-iron tray.

Coke is the best fuel for the indoor stove, and charcoal for
the outdoor one. Coal is not suitable, as it smokes the soldering
bits.

Gas stoves may also be used for heating the bits, and
they possess the advantages of requiring but little attention

G

and of being soon made ready for use ; with a gas stove, also, the solder is not so liable to be burnt off the bit through inattention. A suitable gas stove is illustrated by Fig. 155.

Other requisites besides those named are a jar to hold the spirits or soldering fluid, a file or two, a scraping knife, and one or two brushes for the spirits.   A good brush for the purpose can

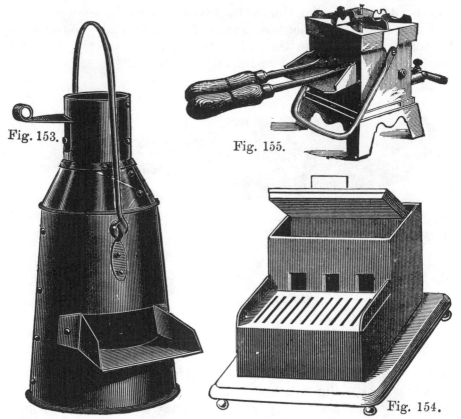

Figs. 153 and 154.—Fire Pots for Heating Bits ; Fig. 155.—Gas Stove for Heating Bits.

be made from a bit of compo tube, a knot of hair out of a broom slipped into the tube, which is flattened with a blow of the hammer.   A suitable "brush" also may be made by hammering the end of a piece of cane until the fibres separate.

Tinmen's solder is composed of lead and tin in varying proportions.   A solder suitable for rough jobbing and outdoor work is made by melting in a ladle 3 lb. of lead and adding 4 lb. of tin ; mix well with a smaller ladle, remove the dross which will float on the top, and run into strips in moulds made by bending some pieces of sheet iron anglewise, and turning the ends so as to prevent the solder running out. These moulds are about 14 in. long, and are shown by Fig. 156. For a finer solder for general purposes, new work, etc., the proportion is 4 of tin to

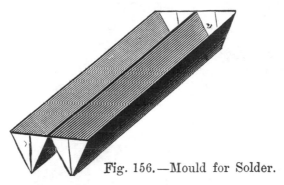

Fig. 156.—Mould for Solder.

2 of lead. For blowpipe solder add one part bismuth to the alloy last mentioned, and run out in fine strips by means of a small iron ladle shaped as in Fig. 157. Ladle out some molten solder, and, holding it over a flat iron plate, which the bottom of the ladle should just touch, cant the solder to flow through the hole, at the same time drawing the ladle from left to right ; a fine

Fig. 157.—Self-skimming Solder Ladle.

stream of solder cools as it touches the cold iron plate, making sticks fit for use with the blowpipe.

Sometimes pewter, an alloy of tin and lead (see page 18) bought in scrap, is used instead of pure lead for making solder. It is obvious that with pewter a smaller quantity of lead must be used than if pure tin were being used. Definite proportions of lead and pewter to make solder cannot be given, as pewters differ in quality. As a general rule, however, it is found undesirable to have a larger proportion of lead than 3 to 10 of pewter.

The following short table gives the compositions and many
of the approximate melting points of soft solders :—

Name.	Lead.	Tin.	Bismuth.	Melting Point.	
				Fah.	Cent.
Soft coarse	2	1	--	440°	227°
Soft fine	1	2	–	340°	174°
Soft fusible	1	2	1	–	–
Tinman's superior ..	2	3	–	334°	167°
Ditto ordinary ...	1	1	–	323°	162°
Bismuth	4	4	1	320°	160°
Ditto	3	3	1	310°	153°
Ditto	2	2	1	292°	144°
Ditto	1	1	1	254° ·	123°
Ditto ... ...。	1	1	2	203°	95°
Pewterer's soft ...	4	3	1	–	–
Ditto ..	4	3	2	–	–
Ditto ...	1	2	1	–	–

To test solder, run a stick of the molten metal, which cools
with a bright silvery appearance. Should it turn a bluish grey,
it contains too much lead ; if a dull white and pitted with little
dots, it contains too much tin. In any case the remedy is
obvious. Another test is to bend a stick of the solder. If it emits
a slight crackling noise, it is good ; but should the crackling noise
be excessive, a little more lead should be added. It is very
important that zinc must not get into the solder, which would
thereby be spoilt, and composition pipe also should be strictly
kept out of the solder.

Attention is now directed to the various fluxes required for
soldering. Soldering fluid is the name often given to the fluxes
used in soft soldering, known as raw and killed spirits. Raw
spirits is muriatic or hydrochloric acid, made by the action of
sulphuric acid on salt, and called by some " spirits of salts." As
it gives off visible vapours, it is also called "smoking salts."
These fumes rust tools and take the colour from clothes. Hydrochloric acid is used by galvanisers and tinners as a bath in which
to prepare the black iron to receive its coating of whiter metals
after the oxide is removed (see Chapter VI.). Raw spirits has
a strong destructive action on zinc, and is used as a flux to solder

that metal and also to solder galvanised ware. When used for soldering zinc the raw spirits is "killed" by dissolving the zinc, and becomes zinc chloride.

The flux in use for soldering nearly all kinds of sheet metals is this zinc chloride. To prepare it, take a large earthenware pan and place a quantity of clean scrap zinc on the bottom. Half fill the pan with muriatic acid, when a dense and irritating vapour rises and continues until it ceases to bubble, when the acid is said to be "killed." The zinc and chlorine are united. Put a slate over the pan and leave it for, say, twelve hours; then pour off the clear liquor and bottle for use.

Killed spirits may be made on a small scale with a penny-worth of muriatic acid and a few zinc slating nails or a piece of sheet zinc. If the acid is not entirely killed by using an excess of zinc, the free acid present may cause a black stain to show on the work when soldering. To prevent this some add a piece of washing soda or sal-ammoniac to neutralise the free acid. It is always best after using strong spirits to wipe with a wet rag and to clean off afterwards. To solder brass, copper, or bright iron, or to tin metals before soldering them, use the killed spirits neat; but where there is but little oxide to overcome, as in tinware, use half water and half spirits; a pointed stick of wood or a small brush (see page 98) will hold enough flux for soft-soldering jobs. Sal-ammoniac, being the chloride of ammonia, forms a useful flux for tinning copper goods.

To solder without acids, fluxes containing carbon are used; these, when heated, flow like a varnish over the surface to be soldered, thus protecting it from the oxygen in the air at a time when metal is most likely to oxidise. If much oxide has already formed on the harder metals, these fluxes cannot remove it, so they are generally used after an article is tinned by an acid process. Resin is the principal flux of this kind, and, when powdered, is very useful for soldering bright tinware; it can be scraped off again, leaving a bright line of solder without fear of rust in its track. Powdered resin and oil are used for best tinware and for soft metal; the mixture can be wiped off while hot, thus avoiding the risk of scratching the work by scraping it. To solder pewter, Britannia metal, and other alloys having a low melting point, use Gallipoli oil or Venice turpentine, which is crude turpentine before the spirit has been distilled off. To solder heavy lead, Russian tallow is generally used with or without resin, while for lead-light soldering a palm-oil candle is recommended as a soldering flux.

Before any soldering can be done the bit must be tinned. To do this, heat it in the fire to blood-red, grip it in a vice, and quickly file the four faces quite bright ; dip the end of the copper bit in killed spirits, rub it on a piece of sal-ammoniac, hold a stick of solder to the point of the bit and melt a little on the lump of sal-ammoniac, rubbing and turning the bit at the same time. If it is hot enough, the solder will flow and coat the face of the copper. Dip it again in the spirits, and the operation is complete. Another method of tinning a bit is with a piece of clean tin-plate, about 4 in. square, nailed to a piece of wood ; heat and file the bit as before, dip the end in killed spirits, and then put a pinch of resin on the tin-plate, melt a little solder on it, and rub the bit briskly on the tin-plate. The solder will quickly flow on the clean part of the soldering bit. Do not make the copper bit red hot after tinning, or the whole process of filing and tinning will have to be repeated.

It should be the aim of the workman to so use the copper bits that they remain tinned, re-tinning involving loss of time and the filing quickly wearing away the copper. Care should be taken that bits are not burnt in the stove.

A few simple soldering exercises will now be given, and though these are directly connected with repairs, yet it must be remembered that the process of soldering in both new work and repairs is the same. The only difference between the two is that it is necessary to spend more time in preparing the surfaces of old work.

Say it is required to repair a tin saucepan having a small hole in the body. If the hole is not visible, locate the leak by trying with water. Then scrape away the dirt for about 1 in. around it, as there may be other holes near. If one only is found, carefully scrape a bright patch about the size of a sixpence, using the file if necessary. Wet the bright part with the spirit brush, heat the copper bit, and melt off from the stick a knob of solder sufficient to cover the hole, and lay the solder on it. Then, with the point of the bit, melt the solder, which will flow over the clean part and adhere to it ; remove the bit, and allow the solder to set. This method may be followed for all ordinary small repairs.

When a large hole has to be repaired, cut a patch of sheet tin to cover it, allowing a good margin. Trim off the sharp corners, and bend the patch to fit the body, then place it in position and mark round it. As before, carefully clean a patch about ¼ in. beyond the mark ; this will allow the solder to flow well under the patch. Brush some spirits on the under side and edges of the patch, hold it firmly in position, and solder. Much solder is not wanted on the outside of the patch, as it will be made quite sound by the solder flowing underneath.

As a rule, saucepans and similar tin utensils commence to leak at the junction of the bottom and the body, and a leak in this position is best repaired from the inside. Thoroughly clean the bruise or crack, as before described, but allow a fair proportion of solder to remain, so that the hole is well covered.

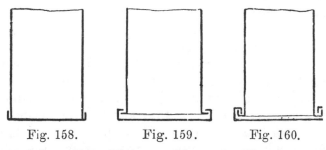

Fig. 158.   Fig. 159.   Fig. 160.

Fig. 158.—Capped-on Bottom ; Fig. 159.—Paned-on Bottom ; Fig. 160.—Knocked-up Bottom.

Hold the article on its edge, and see that the solder is firmly set before moving. When the bottom is rusty inside, and cannot be reached to clean properly, the repair may be done on the outside. When very rusty, brush on a little raw spirit after cleaning ; allow it to remain for a short time, then wipe off with a wet rag. The solder will then adhere much more easily. A cracked bottom edge can be made sound with solder ; first thoroughly clean the edges of the crack, then with the point of the bit draw the solder along the bright part, commencing at one end. In a repair of this kind the solder is liable to melt off in use when brought in direct contact with the fire or hot plate.

When a new bottom is required, it may be "capped on," "paned on," or "knocked up" ; the first two are usually soldered outside, the last inside. A vessel that needs no great strength, or that is not brought into direct contact with heat, such as an ordinary cheap oil-can, frequently has the bottom "capped on,' as in Fig. 158. To re-bottom such a vessel, first scrape the body bright, about ½ in. from the bottom all round, and thoroughly clean the seam. Then hold the can on the edge of the bench, and with a sharp chisel cut off the old bottom carefully, so that the body is not bruised. If drawn out of shape, the body may be rounded again with a mallet on an iron bar or mandrel. The bottom edge, if not true, must be trimmed with the shears. Cut a circle of tin, ¼ in. larger in diameter than the body, and turn up the edge ⅛ in. all round at right angles to the bottom. When completed, this piece should exactly fit on the body, and may then be fixed by the solder being drawn neatly round the joint with the point of the copper bit.

To replace the bottom of a coffee-pot, which is usually " paned on," clean thoroughly, cut off the old bottom, take out the bruises, and trim the edge as in the last case. Then carefully turn the bottom edge of the body outwards, ⅛ in. all round at right angles to the body, making it perfectly level. Cut out a circle of tin for the bottom, allowing ¼ in. for the edge. Turn up the edge of the bottom as before, fit it in position, and rap the edge inwards all round with a small hammer. Then with a pane hammer on a level surface fold the edge of the bottom over the bottom edge of the coffee-pot, and hammer it down close and tight, as in Fig. 159. Solder it carefully on the outside ; the job is then complete.

To replace the " knocked-up " bottom of, say, a saucepan, the old bottom should be cut off and the body trimmed and edged as before described. As the soldering is done from the inside, it must be scraped thoroughly, using the file if necessary, and cleaning a depth of about ¼ in. Cut out, edge, and " pane " on the bottom. Place the saucepan on a mandrel, and with a mallet gradually fold the " paned " edge over square with the body, going round several times if necessary, until the joint is close, as in Fig. 160. The point of the mandrel must be kept well up in the lag, otherwise it may bruise the body, and the bottom will not be true when completed. Dress the bottom smooth with a square-faced hammer, then solder up inside, and the job is completed.

Brazing is another name for hard soldering ; the process differs from ordinary soft soldering principally in the fact that the uniting metal or spelter is not applied with a hot bit. Greater heat is required to melt the spelter than is necessary for soft solder, it being necessary to employ either a forge or a powerful blowpipe to make the hard spelter flow into the joint. Brazing is used where greater strength is required than can be given by soft solder, or when an article has to stand a degree of heat that would cause soft solder to melt.

How to braze a piece of sheet copper in making a tube—this being typical of most of the brazing jobs undertaken by the metal plate worker—will now be described.

In brazing a pipe 12 in. long and 4 in. in diameter, cut the sheet metal to measure 12 in. by a full 13 in. and thin down the two opposite edges (A, Fig. 161, shows one of them) with a crosspane hammer for about ½ in. Notch one side, as shown in Fig. 161, turn it round, bend up the notched pieces x, and slip the other edge in as far as possible, and then knock the notches down and hammer together on a beak iron. Bind round at each end with iron wire, as at Fig. 162, and it is then ready for brazing.

Mix equal parts of spelter and borax in a jar or tray with water, and with the spatula, Fig. 163, spread it on the inside of the joint. The spelter may be an alloy of two parts of copper and one part of zinc. A softer spelter is composed of one part of zinc and one part of copper. The spatula shown in Fig. 163 is very useful in brazing to add a little spelter or borax to the melting spelter, to rub off surplus solder, and to rub it into the joints as it flows. The spatula is made of round iron rod flattened at one end to the shape shown, it being turned into an eye at the other end; two or three of them in different lengths from 12 in. to 20 in. will be handy. Now blow a fire of charcoal or small coke, or of coal cinders; charcoal is a good fuel, but expensive, and the others will do very well. If a coal fire is used, it must be blown perfectly clear, or the smoke will get in the joint and spoil it.

Place the pipe in the forge fire and blow gently. Sprinkle a little powdered borax along the seam, and as the spelter melts rub along with the spatula, drawing out superfluous solder or adding more as may be required. Be careful not to blow too fiercely, as copper will not stand as much heat as iron will, and brass even less heat than will copper. It is at times awkward to braze some articles with a forge, owing to the difficulty of directing the heat to the right place, but this difficulty is overcome by using a gas blowpipe. Where it is possible to do so, small articles should be placed on a piece of charcoal or pumice-stone whilst brazing with the blowpipe; these substances, being low conductors of heat, do not rob the work of the heat imparted to it by the blowpipe flame. A blowpipe for brazing requires a greater pressure of air than can be given by the mouth, so it must be connected to a blower. The air pressure regulates the temperature of the flame, and to get a sharp, concentrated heat an air pressure of from 1 lb. to 1½ lb. on the square inch is required. Such a pressure is easily got from a foot blower.

After using the spatula as described, the application of a little more heat should cause the spelter to run well into the joint. When this is the case remove the work from the forge fire or take away the blowpipe flame, as may be the case, and allow to cool, when superfluous spelter is filed off and the joint finished by light hammering.

From the foregoing it will have been seen that the operation of brazing is a simple one, and requires little more than practice

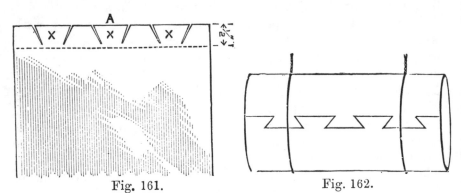

Fig. 161.   Fig. 162.

Fig. 161.—Metal notched for Brazing; Fig. 162.—Pipe in readiness for Brazing.

to be efficiently performed. Brazing as involved in the repair of utensils will now be considered.

A repair very common with copper utensils is to make good a hole worn on the edge of the bottom. This is done by brazing, the process being as follows. Hold the vessel over an open fire or gas blowpipe, and so burn off all grease. Immerse in muriatic acid, and then scour with coke-dust, salt, etc., to remove even a trace of dirt. When this is done, if it is a small pan, dip it in and out of some nitric acid (aquafortis), alternately using hot strong potash water. In about ten minutes the tin inside the vessel will be eaten off, leaving the copper bare. The pan is now ready for brazing, which, as before, is done by using spelter, **mixed wet** with powdered borax, afterwards using some dry powdered borax to throw on as a flux whilst the spelter is melting. The hole to be brazed must be closed up so that the two edges that are worn away overlap one another. Melt the spelter over a sharp, quick fire of small coke, free from any particles of tin that might mix in the coke while burning off. As already mentioned, a gas blowpipe can be used instead of a fire if desired. When the pan is cold, trim the outside where brazed with a coarse file, and finish off with a few blows from the hammer to smooth it down. Where a pan is brazed as described above the copper that is made red-hot naturally becomes softened, and if left without any further treatment would get bruised and knocked out of shape very quickly with wear. To strengthen the copper it is hammered on all those parts touched by the fire or blowpipe flame. The hammering hardens the copper again, and renders it better able to resist hard wear than if left without hammering. The burnt borax is removed by

Fig. 163.—Spatula for applying Spelter

immersing the vessel in a solution of 1 part sulphuric acid and 10 parts water.

When the pan has remained in this dilute acid about half an hour it will be ready for scouring with equal parts of silver sand and common salt applied with a piece of tow ; the borax is then easily removed. Time can be saved by "dipping" the article in aquafortis, this answering the same purpose as scouring with sand and salt. After rinsing the pan with chloride of zinc, it is ready to be tinned as described in Chapter VI.

Vessels of thick copper often require to be re-bottomed, and in most cases the job is done by the raised-brazed method. The sides of saucepans and similar vessels, when of thick copper, will stand as many as three or four new bottoms, and each bottom lasts twice as long as the old style seamed bottoms. Raised-brazed bottoms enable a new brazed bottom to be put on an old pan without the depth being lessened ; in fact, by the raised-brazed method a pan can be made deeper if required. By the old method depth was lost by cutting away the worn bottom and taking up more material for the new seaming edge. The new bottom is raised up similar in shape to an ordinary omelet pan, and the brazing seam is worked on the side instead of the bottom, hence the term raised-brazed.

In raised-brazing a new bottom to a copper saucepan, commence by taking off the handle. Set the pan on a surface plate with its bottom as level as possible, and with a pair of compasses describe a line round the side of the pan high enough up to clear the part that is worn thin. Cut the old bottom off at this line, afterwards heating the pan over a fire and wiping out as much of the old tin as possible with a piece of tow. To complete the removal of the tin, rinse repeatedly with, or immerse in, nitric acid, using hot potash water as before. Then draw down the fresh-cut edge with a thinning hammer ; and if the edge in thinning becomes at all irregular, trim with a file. After rubbing over with wet salt, anneal the copper by bringing it to a red heat and allowing it to cool slowly ; this softens it for further treatment. This process of salting and annealing is known as " pickling off." Now cut the cramps regularly by means of a sharp chisel ; they must not be too large, or the copper will be liable to draw in the brazing.

The cramps have the appearance of teeth, their size varying with the thickness of the pan. They are turned back nearly at right angles to the sides of the pan, so that the bottom, when ready, can fit on, being held in position with strong wire twisted round ; the wire must be kept firm while the cramps are hammered down, and not taken off until after the brazing. The wet spelter should be laid on evenly all round the inside of the cramps by the aid of the spatula, Fig. 163, p. 107, and the whole pan should be gradually warmed to evaporate the water in the borax before any great heat is applied to melt the spelter. Just as the latter runs evenly, draw the pan a little way off the fire so as to allow the molten spelter to settle ; the vessel must not be turned round to the full heat of the fire, or the spelter will run round also. This running of the spelter round the brazing seam must be guarded against. When the pan has been brazed quite soundly, it is finished off precisely as before described.

As has been said, brazing is a simple art ; but, for all that, neat and sound work can only be done as the result of considerable practice.

CHAPTER VI.

TINNING, RE-TINNING, AND GALVANISING.

MANY of the copper utensils formed by the sheet metal worker must have their insides tinned before being brought into domestic use. Besides this tinning of new work, copper and iron pans often require to be re-tinned. The process of tinning in both new and old work is identically the same, but with the latter more time has to be spent in cleansing the metal, and thus preparing it for its coating of tin. New work requires only to be treated with spirits of salt previous to the application of the tinning fluxes.

In commencing to re-tin an article it is desirable to take out all bruises, as then it can be wiped out much better. Bruises may be hammered out on the side and bottom stakes. The method of cleaning to be adopted depends upon the use to which the article has been put. This cleaning must be done to perfection, or it will be impossible to coat the metal with tin.

The usual run of copper utensils, such as stewpans, stock-pots, bain-maries, gravy strainers, etc., are mostly cleaned first by burning off, that is, placing the vessel over a fire and heating it up gradually until all the fat is burnt off from the pan and under the handles. This burning may be done over an ordinary forge fire or in the flame of a gas blowpipe, the vessel being moved about so that the grease from the whole surface is burned off. If the pan is too hot, the copper will soften, and require to be hardened by hammering all over when cool.

The grease may be removed without burning by immersing the vessel in a warm solution of ten parts water and one part caustic soda. To prepare the solution boil the water and stir in the caustic soda with a glass rod. Remove the pan from the solution, quickly rinse in cold water, again immerse in the solution, and then again rinse in water, rubbing with a pad of tow or a fibre brush whilst in the water. All grease should now have been removed.

After the fat has been burnt off or otherwise removed, the next step is to immerse the pan in spirits of salts (muriatic acid) contained in an earthenware vessel. If the pan is very dirty, make it hot and cool it in the acid, being careful not to inhale the fumes that will be given off. Still more vigorous cleansing will be required now, if the pan was overheated when burning off; alternate immersions in nitric acid and spirits of salts, and a scouring with coke-dust, salt, etc., between each immersion being necessary. Having immersed the pan in the spirits of salts, stand it in the open air, and with a mop of old sacking tied on to a stick, keep it well doused with the spirits until the pan is clean ; this may be in a long or a short time, according as to whether the pan were very dirty or only slightly so.

When the pan is clean, rinse in water and scour it with a mixture of equal parts of fine coke-dust, iron scales, and salt, applied with a piece of tow. This scouring must be done very thoroughly, so that all parts of the metal will afterwards take the tin and render unnecessary any touching up with solder. It requires practice to know when a vessel is clean enough for tinning. Attention should be given to the handle and any fittings. The heads of the rivets that secure the handles should be scraped quite clean with a piece of wire, one end of which has been hammered to a chisel shape. If the handle is then loose, tighten it up by hammering the rivet-heads upon a mandrel.

The pan is now ready to be tinned. The outside and those parts not to be tinned must be protected from the oxidizing action of air when the metal is hot by wiping with strong brine (salt and water) or with moist whiting, or with a mixture of salt, whiting, and water. The border or rim of a copper stewpan should not be so coated, as it is to be tinned. Allow the coating to dry before proceeding further. Rinse the surface to be tinned with clean chloride of zinc (killed spirits), and sprinkle with finely powdered sal-ammoniac; these fluxes prevent the oxidation of the copper and tin when hot. Take care to prepare the rim for tinning ; the depth of the latter may be marked round with a pair of compasses. The pan should now be heated uniformly over a forge fire or large blowpipe flame until a stick of pure tin, which is rubbed upon the inner surface, melts at the end. The molten metal is quickly diffused over the parts to be tinned with a pad of wool or tow ; take care to properly tin the rivets,

or they might possibly leak. If the vessel is thoroughly clean
there will be no difficulty in tinning and wiping it out in one
heat. With cotton-wool and a little sal-ammoniac wipe out very
carefully, and then cool the pan in plenty of clean water. If the
pan were allowed to cool slowly out of the water, it would have
a dull, discoloured appearance, instead of a silver colour.

Small patches, where the tin did not adhere, will become
evident if the copper was not well cleaned. These patches may
be touched up by well rubbing with a lump of sal-ammoniac
while the tin is in a molten condition. On cooling, again
immerse the pan and wash off the burnt whiting which was
applied to protect the outside of the pan. With a wisp of tow
scour the inside with silver sand, rinse in water, and wash the
outside with a solution of cyanide of potassium ; this is a deadly
poison, and should be applied with tow on the end of a stick,
keeping the hands free from it. If the pan was not made too
hot in tinning, this solution will instantly remove all dirt, and
give the copper its original bright colour. A piece of cyanide
about as large as a walnut is sufficient for a pint of water.

After cleansing the pan with the cyanide solution, rinse with
water, and clean the rivets with silver sand, using a brush and
a sharp-pointed stick. When the handle and rivets are thoroughly
clean, scour the outside of the pan, and then with a fresh piece
of tow and fresh silver sand finish off the inside, finally removing
all stains from the fire, flux, etc. The sand should be worked
round in one direction only to give a neater appearance ; an even
mark on the bottom of the inside is made by rubbing with
a cork.

When vessels of intricate shapes are to be tinned, and it is
found impossible to wipe them out as before described, they are
heated to a temperature a little above the melting point of tin,
flux is thrown in as usual, and the molten tin is poured in from
a ladle, the article being then tilted about over the fire or blowpipe flame until the whole inner surface is coated ; superfluous
tin is then poured out. Another method is to coat the outside
with whiting, and, holding the vessel with a pair of tinner's tongs,
immerse it in molten tin, tilting it so as to allow the spare tin
to drain out.

Wrought-iron vessels are re-tinned in practically the same
manner as are copper ones. First scour the article with sand
and water, immerse in warm dilute hydrochloric acid until the

surface to be tinned is clean and free from black patches, and then scour again with pumice-stone and water. Then proceed exactly as with the copper pan, though if it is convenient the vessel may be immersed in molten tin instead. When immersing the pan, the open top should be held farthest from the worker, as the molten metal in contact with the damp surface boils and "spits."

By galvanising is meant merely the application of a coat of zinc which alloys with the surface of the metal to which it is applied. Thus the material known as "galvanised iron" is sheet steel (which has superseded iron) upon which has been deposited a film of zinc. Metal in sheet, galvanised before it is worked up, is treated generally by a method different from that adopted for vessels, utensils, etc., but there is no reason why the following process should not be suitable for galvanising both metal in sheet and the articles into which it is formed. The success of the process, as in tinning metals, depends on the thoroughness with which the metal is cleansed previous to being passed through the molten zinc. The plates or vessels are first immersed in a warm bath of equal parts of sulphuric or muriatic acid and **water**, being afterwards scoured with emery or sand. They are now ready for the preparing bath, made by mixing together equal parts of saturated solutions of chloride of zinc and chloride of ammonium. The metallic bath through which they are next passed is a molten alloy of 640 parts (by weight) of zinc, 106 parts of mercury, and $\frac{1}{3}$ part of sodium. Throw some sal-ammoniac on the top of the bath, previously skimming off any oxide that might have formed, and immerse the articles, bringing the temperature up to 680° F. Remove the articles directly this heat is attained, otherwise the zinc will dissolve a portion of the iron. Zinc has a great affinity for iron, and it is a good plan to partly satisfy this by allowing the molten zinc to previously act on a piece of waste wrought-iron.

Small articles of solid iron or steel are galvanised preferably by the following method. The articles are cleansed in a revolving barrel or tumbling box containing sand, which chafes the iron and removes scale, etc. A solution is made by saturating with sheet zinc 10 parts of hydrochloric acid, and, when the evolution of gas has ceased, dissolving in it 1 part of muriate or sulphate of ammonia. The iron articles are heated and plunged in this solution for an instant; if of the right heat, they will dry at once on removal and be covered with crystals. Prepare a bath of molten zinc as before, removing all oxide and throwing in plenty of sal-ammoniac to stop further oxidation. Heat the articles, dip them whilst quite dry into the zinc, shake off superfluous metal, and cool in water. Small articles may be held in a wrought-iron basket when dipping into the zinc.

It may have been noticed that the process of galvanising proper in both of these two methods is the same, the only difference being in the cleansing processes preceding the galvanising. Two or three more methods of preparing the iron or steel for the galvanising bath may now be noted. (*a*) Immerse the iron articles for a few hours in muriatic acid diluted with twice its weight of water, and then wash thoroughly in hot water and scrub with brush and sand. The final preparation for the bath of molten zinc is immersion in a hot solution of 1 lb. of sal-ammoniac to 2 gallons of water. Dry before galvanising. (*b*) First remove all scale by passing through a bath of 1 part of muriatic acid and 4 parts of water. After brushing and scraping, pass through a fresh bath of 1 part of muriatic acid, 4 parts of water, and 1 oz. of sal-ammoniac to every gallon of solution, and then dry in a hot oven. (*c*) Scour with sand all scale and rust from the surface of the metal, and remove all grease and oil by boiling in a solution of caustic soda. Immerse in dilute muriatic acid, scrub with a metallic brush, and rinse in hot water, afterwards drying thoroughly. The molten metal is liable to "spit" if the article is passed into it wet. It is even possible for slight explosions to occur if moisture is left among laps and rivets.

Perhaps the most general method of galvanising sheet steel or iron is the one by which the metal first receives a preparatory coat of tin. The sheet metal is passed through baths of dilute muriatic acid, scoured with sand and otherwise made perfectly clean. A bath is prepared in a wooden vat by adding 1 part of a saturated solution of metallic tin in concentrated muriatic acid to 600 or 800 parts of water. The preparation of the tin solution occupies from two to three days. At the bottom of the vat is a thin layer of finely-granulated zinc, on top of this being a clean iron or steel plate, which in its turn is covered with granulated zinc, and so on until the bath is full. The zinc, iron, and solution form a weak galvanic battery, tin being deposited from the solution on the iron plates, a coat sufficiently thick for the purpose being obtained in about two hours. The plates are

H

removed, and immediately carried by rollers through a bath of molten zinc covered with a thick layer of sal-ammoniac mixed with earthy matter to lessen its volatilisation. The speed with which the ,rollers revolve practically determines the thickness of the zinc coat on the plates. Owing to the under coating of tin, galvanised plates prepared by this process have a crystalline appearance.

Not only steel and iron, but brass and copper utensils are often galvanised ; there are two or three processes by which this can be done, though they are chemical rather than metallurgical. A simple method is to boil the brass or copper in a solution of chloride of zinc, adding at the same time a small quantity of zinc turnings to the solution. Boettger's process is to cover granulated or powdered zinc, contained in a wooden vessel, with a concentrated solution of sal-ammoniac. Heat to about boiling-point, and immerse the copper or brass articles, which should be chemically clean. A firm coating of zinc will be deposited in a few minutes.

CHAPTER VII.

EXAMPLES OF PRACTICAL METAL PLATE WORK.

To describe the multifarious articles made by the worker in sheet metal would be impossible, so some typical examples are selected, by the study of which the workman will be able to understand the making of things of similar shape and use.

A few examples of square and oblong work will be given first. Say it is required to make a rectangular vessel, Fig. 164, of given dimensions with upright sides in one piece ; it is supposed that this is to be a plain tin pan without wire or fold. Let the size of the vessel be, for example, 8 in. by 5 in. by 2 in. In marking out the plate, add twice the depth of one side to the length and to the width. Thus in this case the size of the plate will be 12 in. by 9 in. Mark out a rectangle of that size on the metal, A B C D, Fig. 165. Set the compasses to the depth required (2 in.), place one point at the corners successively and measure off ; through the points made, draw lines parallel to the outside edges to show the fold for the sides (see Fig. 165). If the sides are to be simply joined by solder, the angle pieces of the pattern must be cut out ; if the sides are to be lapped round at the ends, leave pieces as shown by the dotted lines. If the pan is to be wired along its edge, allow parallel to the outside edges as much extra as will be required for the size of wire to be used. Wiring increases the article in its outside dimensions— though not in its capacity—by twice the thickness of the wire and of the metal that covers it. Thus, in the example just given, instead of the vessel being 8 in. by 5 in., it would be, say, 8¼ in. by 5¼ in. over all. So when an article of this description is to be made of a given dimensions outside the wire, the bottom must be marked smaller all round by the thickness of the wire to be used, and a trifle more to allow for the thickness of the tin.

When the article is to be larger at the top than at the bottom, the sheet metal is cut as in Fig. 166, which shows a pattern for an article the same size as Fig. 164 at the bottom and same depth of sides, but larger at the top by 1 in. each way. After marking the corners out square as in the previous example, set the compasses to half the additional measurement required at the top, and from the points A, A, B, B, C, C, and D, D, mark off points E, E, G, G, H, H, F, F ; lines drawn from these points to the corners X give the required pattern ; the four corner pieces,

Fig. 164.—Upright-sided Rectangular Vessel.

Fig. 166, are cut away. Oil tanks for stoves are marked out in this way, only then the part here called the bottom would be the top, and the bottom would be soldered in at the large part.

A view of a Yorkshire pudding dish is given by Fig. 167, and

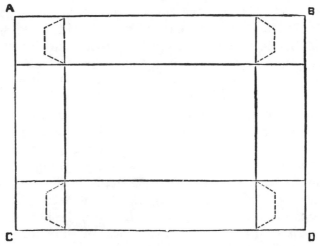

Fig. 165.—Pattern for Upright-sided Rectangular Vessel.

the method of marking it out is made clear in Fig. 168, which shows a full-sized corner. For stock sizes the pans are usually cut out of the full-size tin plate, and are turned up from 1½ in. to 1¾ in. before wiring. The marking out is done in a similar way to that described for Fig. 166, but after marking the points, which give the difference in size between the top and the bottom, a line is drawn at right angles to the edge, and the notch cut to allow for wiring; this notch is cut rather

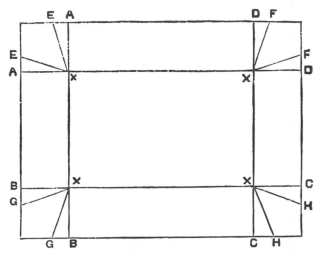

Fig. 166.—Pattern for Rectangular Sloping-sided Vessel.

deeper than twice the diameter of the wire to be used. The dotted line, A, B, shows the part to be turned over the wire. The compasses are then placed at the corners x with radius x A, and the arc A C described, the portion F being then cut away. In working up corners great care must be taken to get them

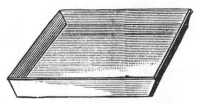

Fig. 167.—Pudding Dish.

true. The way to do it is this : press the corners over the tip of the extinguisher stake and bend on the line E X; this will commence the corners and slightly turn up the side, which can then be continued on the hatchet stake or, if that is too wide, on the side of the anvil or end of the crease iron, assisted by the mallet. When the sides are bent up sufficiently the corners are knocked together to make A and C meet, and then bent round on the ends of the pan, against which they should lie quite close and flat. The edges can next be folded on the hatchet for wiring, then wired and jennied, which completes the dishes, as they

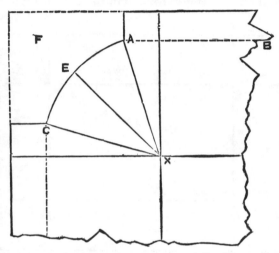

Fig. 168.—Pattern for Corner of Pudding Dish.

require no solder when the corners are turned up in this way. A special tool for commencing to turn up the sides is called a dripping-pan swage ; this can be set to various depths, and is very useful for quick work.

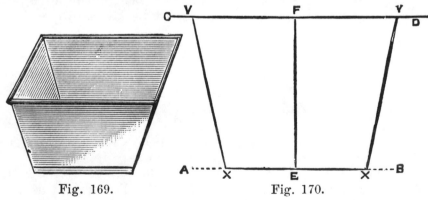

Fig. 169.

Fig. 169.—Bread Tin ; Fig. 170.—Pattern of End of Bread Tin.

In making square articles with the sides and bottoms in separate pieces, as, for example, bread tins (Fig. 169), mark out the end pattern, Fig. 170; set out a line, A B, and erect the perpendicular, E F; this latter is as long as the dish is to be deep.   Draw C D parallel to A B.   On each side of the perpendicular, E F, line set off on A B a distance equal to half the width required at the bottom of the tin x x, and from the point F, set off on each side half the width required at

Fig. 171.--Pattern of Side of Bread Tin.

top of tin, V V.   Join V X on each side of the perpendicular line, and the lines will show a true and correct pattern.   The pattern for the side, Fig. 171, is drawn in exactly the same way. Allowance for edge wiring and for seaming the bottom should be added to the pattern, as shown by the dotted lines, after marking the net finished size.   The end pattern will require for wire and bottom edge the same allowance, but at the sides it will require only half as much.   This is because the sides are

Figs. 172 and 173.—Sections of Folds.

knocked round on to the ends, and thus gives a double turn on the side portion, thus requiring a larger allowance.   If the ends were to be knocked on to the sides, the side pattern would would have the small allowance and the ends the large one.

Articles of this shape are very easy to make.   Place all the cut out sides and ends at the folding machine.   Take the sides first, seam and fold them close up, both folds one way, as shown by the section line of fold, Fig. 172.   Next fold over the ends a right angle, instead of close as in the case of the sides.   This is shown by the section line, Fig. 173.   Next fold for wiring. The ends must be put into the machine with the fold upwards, and the sides with the fold downwards. If the cutting out is absolutely true, the edge for the bottoms can also be folded in the machine. It will be best, if there is any doubt, after they are put together and wired to throw off the edge. To do this,

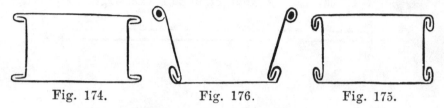

Fig. 174.   Fig. 176.   Fig. 175.

Figs. 174–176.—Sections through Bread Tin.

take a side and end, and slip the side into the end, and keeping it in position with the forefinger, pane them together, using a beak iron for this ; then knock this seam down on the end ; this leaves the edge rather rounding. To square it up, hold the seam edgeways on the beak iron and go along the rounding edge with

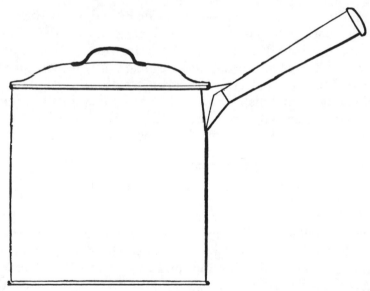

Fig. 177.—Saucepan.

a square-faced hammer ; treat all like this, and then put the halves together in the same way.

Figs. 174 and 175 show horizontal cross-sections of the tin, with seams paned and knocked up. Next wire the top and edge the bottoms. Cut bottoms with sufficient allowance for turn up, notch all four corners, turn up on the hatchet, and pane and knock up as usual. Square the knocking up with the hammer in

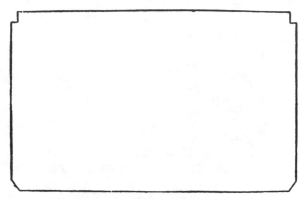

Fig. 178.—Pattern of Saucepan Body.

a similar manner to that described above. Fig. 176 is a vertical section showing seaming of bottom.

As an example of saucepan work, a two-quart saucepan (Fig. 177), may be made; such a saucepan is about 6 in. in diameter and the same in depth. Its patterns in the sheet

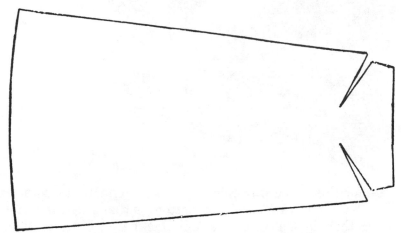

Fig. 179.—Pattern of Saucepan Handle.

metal are shown by Figs. 178 to 183. They consist of saucepan body (Fig. 178), handle (Fig. 179), boss (Fig. 180), apron (Fig. 181), notch pattern (Fig. 182), and cover handle (Fig. 183). The bottom and cover do not require patterns, as they are struck out with the compasses ; and the rim of the cover is marked out by means of a flue rim, made as described on p. 129. Referring to the body pattern given by Fig. 178, it will be noticed that each corner is notched. The notches at the top are for the seam and wire, and they are cut longer one way than the other ; the

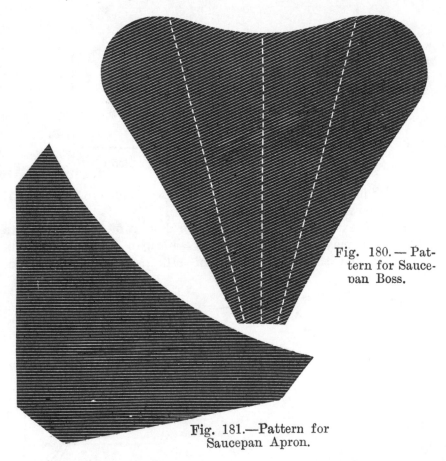

Fig. 180. — Pattern for Saucepan Boss.

Fig. 181.—Pattern for Saucepan Apron.

reason for this is the wire fold requires more metal than the seam fold. The notches are cut at the bottom so that after the seams are put together there shall not be four thicknesses of metal plate.

The body, if cut out of single plates, will be in two pieces, and if cut out of 20-in. plates, in one piece. For the sake of the example of grooving two pieces together, it is supposed that two plates are to be used. Laying the pattern on the tin plate will show that two pieces can be got out of each sheet, leaving a narrow piece, which will do for the rim—thus one plate will cut the body and rim.   The cover, bottom, and small work will be marked out when required.   When many are made

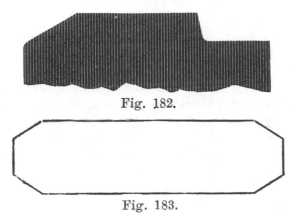

Fig. 182.

Fig. 183.

Fig. 182.—Notch Pattern; Fig. 183.—Pattern for Cover Handle.

at a time, it is best to cut out with the stock shears, as two or three tin sheets can be cut out at one time, and then only the top one of each lot need be marked.   To keep the tin plates from shifting, they are cut in convenient places and twisted over and hammered down to form "ties."   An example

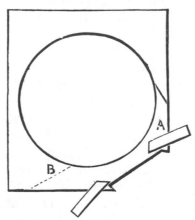

Fig. 184.—Method of "Tying" when cutting several Thicknesses.

of this is shown by Fig. 184.   Commence to cut the circle at A, in the direction shown, and the ties then hold the plates together till the cut has been made right round to B ; if the cut commenced as shown at B, the ties would be cut off before the circle was completed. Great care must be taken to get all edges quite straight, or trouble will occur when they are being folded in the machine. Having cut out the body parts, pass them through the rollers to break the "grain" of the metal. Set the front roller so as not to pinch the plates ; pass them through six pieces at a time, setting the back roller down till the pieces roll out in a semicircle ; turn them over, replace in the rollers, bend down so as to allow the plates to catch under, and pass them through once more ; again turn over and place between the front rollers, raise the back roller two or three turns and pass through, and the plates will then come out straight. By this means the plates, when wired and turned round, do not present a ribbed appearance, which looks very bad : where rollers are not available the grain may be taken out on the former, Fig. 142, p. 90, or even across the knee ; by the latter plan the "burr" of the tin is apt to cut the apron or trousers.

Fig. 185.—Section of Folded Body.

The next operation is folding the bodies for seaming and wiring. Place the body pieces on the left of the folding machine with the top notches from the workman ; this is especially important when the articles are to be lap-wired, which is the most workmanlike method. Set the machine to fold a trifle over $\frac{1}{8}$ in. ; a large fold makes an ugly seam. Raise the front roller of the machine to give a close, flat fold ; place a body piece in, press it close to the guide-plate, raise the handle of the machine, keep the plate in place with the left hand, let it come up as far as it will, and then lower it on to the bench, when the folded piece will slip out easily. The other end of this piece must be folded on the opposite side (Fig. 185), or the two pieces will not be in right positions for seaming together. When both are done, the pieces must be folded for wiring with No. 10 or 11 gauge wire. Set a pair of compasses to twice the diameter of the wire, and at that distance from the edge mark a line on the tin, and set the machine till it just allows the line to disappear, and this time lower the front roller to give a rounding fold. Raise the handle only half the distance, as for wiring the fold does not require to be brought over so far. Should any piece slip out of the machine, either when folding the seams or the wiring, it must be finished on the hatchet stake; should a folding machine not be available, the whole of the folding must be done on the stake, and in that case, when folding the seams, the notches must be kept towards the workman.

The grooving together of the body pieces, the next operation, is best done on a bench plate, which is a plate of cast iron planed smooth and about ½ in. or ⅜ in. in thickness and from 12 in. to 15 in. square. With the wire fold towards the worker, slip one fold over the other, and with a groover, Fig. 126, p. 85, of suitable size placed on the seam, form the groove by striking it with a mallet, moving it up and down the seam and increasing the weight of the blows until the seam is properly formed, as shown by the section of seam, Fig. 186. It may then be closed with light blows of the square-faced hammer.

The next operation is to wire the bodies; this can be done on the bench plate or on the crease iron. Take a roll of wire

Fig. 186.—Section of Grooved Seam.

and begin ½ in. to ¾ in. from the end of the fold at the right-hand end of the body; hold the wire in position with the thumb while knocking down the fold to fix the wire, then proceed along the body. The curved shape of the wire assists in keeping it close to the tin, and as the wiring proceeds the body piece may curve to the shape of the wire; but this will not matter, as it has to be rolled. After wiring all along, cut off the wire, leaving at the left-hand end as much extra wire as was left out on the left-hand end. Pass all the bodies through the jenny to smooth down the wiring, which up to this has a puckered appearance. Commence at the end nearest to the worker; turn the handle and slightly raise the body; the wheels should have grip enough to draw it through; if not, tighten both screws half a turn. The wire will then be neatly tucked in and smoothed. Rolling comes next. Set the top front roller so as to allow the seam to go between it and the bottom one without being flattened; lower the back roller to give sufficient curve to make the body circular. Place a body piece between the rollers, with the wire in one of the grooves in the top roller; if the circle is too large, depress the back roller, and if too small raise it. The body will require pulling to the right as it goes through, as there is always a tendency to draw to the left.

Shaping and seaming will be the next job. In practice a certain amount of shaping has to be done always; perhaps, owing to one-half of the body being a little thinner than the other half, it has bent more, or other causes may necessitate shaping, which is done partly before grooving the second seam and partly afterwards. To groove the two halves together, use the side stake. Open the wire fold where there is no wire in it and where it has been pressed down by the roller, lay in the piece

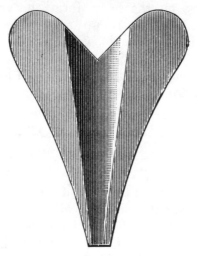

Fig. 187.—Rough Boss of Saucepan.

of wire that projects from the other side and tuck it in smoothly, place it on the tool with the wire part towards the worker, and groove the seam in the way described for the first one.

Edging the bodies is the next process, which may be done with the stock shears or the jenny, or the hatchet may be used when there is no other tool to do it with. Edging with the jenny is an easy and quick method. The bottom of the body must be trimmed quite true at the seams, or the edge will be unequal. The guide of the jenny is screwed back to leave about ⅛ in. or less of the back part of the bottom wheel, the saucepan body is inserted and the top screw tightened down enough to prevent its slipping out as it turns round. The body is held lightly by the wire and pressed from the worker **and in towards** the guide, but not too hard, or the size of the edge will increase. An edge ⅛ in. wide is sufficient for this size article ; more would necessitate a larger bottom and make a clumsy-looking turn up.

Next mark out the bottoms to allow as much turn up as there is edge. The size of the bottom, when found and proved correct, should be marked with the compass on the body pattern ; these marks are not shown in Fig. 178, p. 121. The mode of putting on the "knocked-up" bottom of a saucepan has already been described in Chap. V., pp. 103 and 104.

Attention can be given now to the small work, commencing with the handle, Fig. 179. After cutting out the pieces to shape,

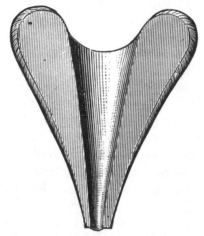

Fig. 188.—Finished Boss of Saucepan.

turn them on the beak iron. Some workmen work with the point of the beak iron pointing away, but others use it with the point towards them. With the mallet bend one edge slightly on the tool, then, grasping the handle and tool together with the right hand, bend the handles round the tool about two-thirds the required distance ; then bend the other edge with the mallet as before, and finish bending them round, making the lap about ¼ in. The flap must be left flat ; after the handle is turned it is bent back, and with a small hammer tapped close to the handle. Next, with a suitable size hollow punch, punch out some studs and hollow them with the stud boss and punch, or with a stud hammer on the lead piece ; these studs must be edged on a small stool, slipped on the handle and soldered. The flaps of the handles can then be knocked back and fitted to shape.

The boss, Fig. 180, is held on the hatchet stake at the dotted lines, and is struck a blow or two. The flaps are then bent down, next turned over, placed on the tool in the centre of the boss, and pressed down each side ; this roughly shapes them. They are finished on the extinguisher stake¯ with the mallet, and the outside edges are very slightly bevelled. Fig. 187 shows the boss as it comes from the hatchet ; Fig. 188 shows it when finished. The apron and cover handle are folded with a small fold, and then the apron is false wired by being held on the hatchet with thumb and finger, and tapped lightly all along with a mallet, the folded part being allowed to just lap over the edge of the tool ; on turning it over it will have the appearance of being wired. Cover handles are frequently treated in the same way. It does very well for common goods, but good work ought to be wired with 15 or 16 gauge wire. The tip of the apron should be bent back slightly with the mallet, and the hollowed out part slightly bevelled on the hatchet with the round end of the mallet.

The small work is now ready to be fixed to the saucepan. The handle is first tacked to the saucepan by a drop of solder placed so as to fix the points of the handle and the flap to the body at the seam that was last grooved ; next place the boss in its place behind the handle and tack that also top and bottom. Next solder on the apron ; place it so that the point is in the centre of the handle and the wide part just below the level of the top of the saucepan, and fasten it with a drop of solder on the point, then solder along the flap. Next rivet the two ears of the boss, and the flap of the handle which is beneath them ; rather small rivets, about 14 oz., will do very well. Place a rivet on the tool, and on it the saucepan ; tap with the hammer, and the position of the rivet will be shown by a mark. Place the rivet set, Fig. 127, p. 85, with its hole over the mark, and draw the rivet through by hammering the set ; hammer the rivet to a head, and finish with the button or countersunk side of the rivet set. Follies may be used for punching such rivet holes, and where much riveting has to be done they are very useful. After riveting, the boss has to be soldered round. Commence at the left-hand side with plenty of solder, well run in at the joint of the handle with the saucepan, and lead the solder down one side of the boss and up the other, well soaking the sides, and then over the bridge of the boss.

Of the cover, the rim is the first part to be made ; the pieces for it come off the body. The rim is marked out by means of a home - made tool called a flue-rim, as previously mentioned. The object of cutting the rims slightly tapering instead of straight is that a better fit may be made, and they are easier to put on and take off. To make the flue-rim, take a pair of long-legged compasses, set them to a radius of 5 ft. or 5 ft 6 in., and on a strip of tin 2 in. wide and 20 in. long draw an arc. If, instead of the compasses, string or wire is used, make a loop in one end and place it over a bradawl stuck in the floor, and with another awl at the other end describe the arc ; cut the tin plate along the line very carefully, fold over the straight-edge and knock down with the mallet ; this gives a short straightedge and flue-rim combined, and a rule also ; set out and stamp the figures on it. This flue-rim pattern will do for straight-sided round articles, and for those larger at the bottom than at the top, but for those that taper smaller at bottom, such

Fig. 189.—Part of Cover Rim.

as slop pails, a pattern with a smaller radius must be used, or the rim binds against the sides of the article before it is fully down to the wire.

To mark out the rims, place the flue-rim on the piece of plate to be used as near the top as possible and scribe a line ; with the compasses at the ends mark off the width required for the rim and scribe lines through these marks with the flue-rim as a guide. The procedure in making a dozen rims from a sheet of tin is the same. When all the rim pieces are cut out, point one end as shown in Fig. 189. Two pieces can next be soldered together, and for this a fairly flat and smooth board will be wanted. Take the flue-rim and with an awl scribe a line across it, place one of the rim pieces with its pointed end over the blunt end of the other and solder together, holding them down with an awl or piece of wood till cool.

The rims must be folded on the hatchet, as owing to their curvature it cannot be done in a machine. It is usual to do two at a time, but beginners should try one first. Rims are folded on

I

the inner curve ; a full ⅛ in. will be about right for this size, but for larger rims make larger folds ; let them pass under the left arm ; commence at the blunt end, so that when folded the solder is outside. Go over it twice, then hammer flat on the crease iron and bend round two at a time in the rollers. The ends of them will require rounding up before tacking to the size of the saucepan. To do this, place a rim in a saucepan, make it a comfortable fit, and draw it out carefully and tack the outside ; replace it to see that it has not shifted, and then tack inside ; some cut off all superfluous lengths, but some think it better to leave them, as they strengthen the rim. The next process is to edge the rims, which will be done in the jenny, the same as the bodies were. The covers must then be marked and cut out, allowing more margin than for the bottoms because of the doming or hollowing ; about ¼ in. all round larger than the outside of the rim is sufficient, and after the covers have been hollowed and found to be correct in size, mark this on the body pattern in the same way as mentioned for the bottom.

The hollowing or blocking of the covers, the next operation, is one which requires much skill and practice to perform successfully. The block should be of a tough and close-grained wood, such as beech, walnut, or apple, and not less than 15 in. in diameter at the bottom. The top must be sawn off smooth and level, but need not be planed. It should be about the height of the bench. If intended to work at it standing, as many do, it may be a couple of inches higher, and if sitting down to it a little lower. To get it ready for use, take a good sized hollowing hammer, and about 3 in. from the edge hammer a depression ; this latter must be deepest on the edge where it is about ⅜ in. deep, the heel of the hammer doing most of the work ; the hole is shallow towards the centre of the block, but it will get deeper by frequent use. Another hollow may be made, a little shallower than the first. Covers for new work are hollowed up four or six at a time, according to the thickness of the plate. Covers of 1 c and 1 x may be hollowed in lots of six ; when of 1 xx or 1 xxx tin plate, four at a time will be enough. Before commencing to block up, describe a circle a little less than one-third of the diameter. It is a guide to the limit of the hollowing, as saucepan covers are not hollowed right to the centre, though a tea-kettle cover would be ; see Figs. 190 and 191, which give a section through the centre, showing the difference between the hollowing of a saucepan and a tea-kettle cover. Commence by grasping the lot of covers at A, Fig. 192, thumb inside, and hold them over the shallower hole, so that the part marked 1 in the circle comes just over the middle of it ; then give firm blows of the hammer as shown, 1, 2, 3, 1, 2, 3, 1, 2, 3, working in the direction shown by the arrow, and proceeding all round. The covers will have hollowed considerably, but may present a very puckered appearance, which may cause the beginner some misgivings as to his ever being able to get them smooth ; but patience and perseverance will accomplish this.

To finish the hollowing, hammer round in circles as shown by

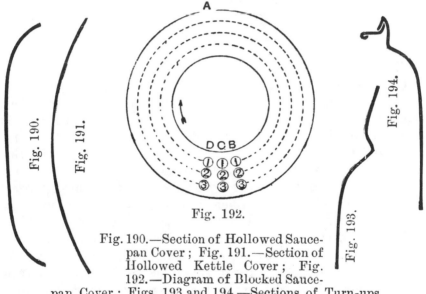

Fig. 192.

Fig. 190.—Section of Hollowed Saucepan Cover ; Fig. 191.—Section of Hollowed Kettle Cover ; Fig. 192.—Diagram of Blocked Saucepan Cover ; Figs. 193 and 194.—Sections of Turn-ups.

the dotted rings in the order marked, 1, 2, 3 ; finally transfer the covers to the deeper hole. Having hollowed the lids, next smooth them off ; this is done with a hammer having a slightly flatter face, especially for the centre part of the cover. Most workmen, before commencing to smooth, shake the covers apart and turn each round a little way so that the puckers are not opposite one another. Commence working from the inner circle outwards on a flat place on the block, and finish at the edges with the hollowing hammer.

The flange is now thrown back in the jenny ; for the covers under consideration the width will be about ⅜ in. Place the cover between the wheels and screw down, not tightly, and holding the cover the same as for jennying up a bottom, work round carefully once ; run it round several times, gradually raising the flange till it assumes the shape shown by the section line, Fig. 193. Do the inner cover—the one nearest the hammer ; first offer the rim to it, and when it is the right size and shows sufficient to allow for the turn up, the other covers can be jennied. The outer one may want a little trimming, because each one nearer the outside is slightly larger ; but there is generally a little variation in the rims which makes up for this.

To turn over the second edge which covers the flange on the rim (see section, Fig. 194), proceed as in turning up a bottom. If a rim is too large to get in, the turned-up edge of the cover may be rapped back slightly ; and if necessary, the rims pared a little. After paning down on the beak iron, get ready the handle.

The cover handle, Fig. 183, p. 123, is folded and a small wire put in, or it may be false wired as described for the apron. The correct position for the handle is found by describing a circle in the centre of the cover, of a diameter equal to the width of the handle outside the flaps. It is bent into semicircular form, the flaps straightened on each side and soldered to the cover by tacking each under the handle. Put a small rivet through each flap, using one of the round heads or a block hammer fixed in the vice as a support, and the saucepan is then complete.

The fishing-can, the patterns of which are shown by Figs. 232 to 234, pp. 150 and 151, may be taken as the last example for practice. To make the body a small fold is formed along the dotted line A a (Fig. 234, p. 151), and knocked down smoothly on each of the four pieces. Then the pieces along the line B are bent to form the angle shown at B on the elevation, Fig. 232, and the metal is curved in the rollers similar to the shape shown in the latter figure. The four pieces are fitted at the mitred corners and soldered together. Turn up a small edge upon each side of the bottom to fit close to the body, and solder the bottom on. A pair of stout ears are riveted upon the body as shown for the handle. For the cover, cut out a narrow rim, and bend it to fit close inside the top ; perforate the cover and edge it up to fit the rim, then pane it down smooth. The handle is a narrow strip wired along each side, bent to any convenient shape and loosely riveted to ears.

CHAPTER VIII.

EXAMPLES OF PRACTICAL PATTERN DRAWING.

THE preliminary exercises given in Chapters II. and III. having served their purpose, this chapter will be devoted to a number of problems illustrative of practical pattern drawing as applied to some of the many articles in everyday use made in metal plate.

To set out pattern for square baking-pan.—In setting out the pattern for a square baking-pan, first draw two lines at right angles, as A a and BB, Fig. 195. Make BB equal to the length of the top of the pan, and A a equal to the slant length

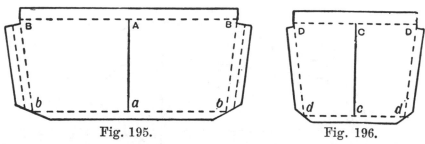

Fig. 195. Fig. 196.

Figs. 195 and 196.—Side and End Patterns for Square Baking-pan.

of the side ; draw through a a line parallel to BB, and make b b equal to the length of the bottom of the pan. Join B b, B b. Then make an allowance for wiring at the top of the pattern, an allowance along the bottom for edging, and also at both ends for a double fold as shown. For the end pattern, commence as for the side, making D D, Fig. 196, equal to the top width of the pan, and C c equal to A a, Fig. 195. Draw through c a line parallel to D D, and from D on both sides drop lines D d, D d, making the same angle with D D as B b does with B B, Fig. 195. Next make allowances at top and bottom as on Fig. 195, and only for a single fold on the sides as shown. The bottom pattern would be a rectangle equal in length and width to b b, d d, with an extra allowance for a double fold on all four sides.

To set out pattern for scale scoop.—To set out the pattern of a scoop for a pair of scales first draw an elevation and plan of the

required size and shape, as Figs. 197 and 198 ; from Q erect a perpendicular c D, and continue it to intersect the top of large arc at 1,
Fig. 197. Divide the arc into any convenient number of equal
parts, say from 1 to 8, and mark off along A B, Fig. 198, a corresponding number of similar parts from Q to 8. This would be
theoretically correct as radius for the larger end of the pattern.
In practice, the copper or other metal employed would stretch
in the hollowing, and, consequently, a little shorter radius, say

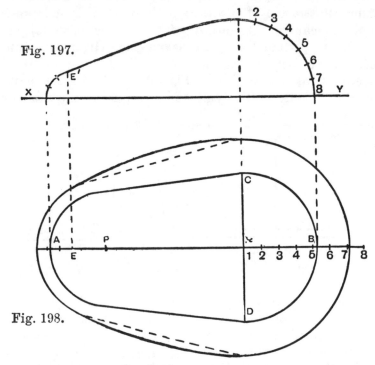

Figs. 197 and 198.—Scale Scoop Elevation and Pattern.

Q 7, may be used for drawing the semicircle. Mark a point (E')
upon the elevation where the small arc joins the straight part,
and drop a perpendicular to E, Fig. 198. Divide the arc into
three equal parts, as shown, and transfer these divisions to the
line A B from E ; then, using P as centre and radius to the
farthest division, describe an arc. On each side of Fig. 198
draw a dotted line to touch the arcs forming the ends, and then
make a full line outside the dotted line, as shown. For hollow
articles with straight sides some allowance is always necessary,

otherwise the edge will be concave instead of straight when the scoop is hollowed to the correct depth.

To set out pattern for an elliptical pan of equal slant.— To set out the elliptical plan of the pan, use approximate method 1, given in Problem 25, p. 41. The construction lines are shown in Fig. 199, A B being the length and C D the width of the pan at the top. The inner ellipse, drawn similarly, represents the plan of the bottom. The pan is composed of

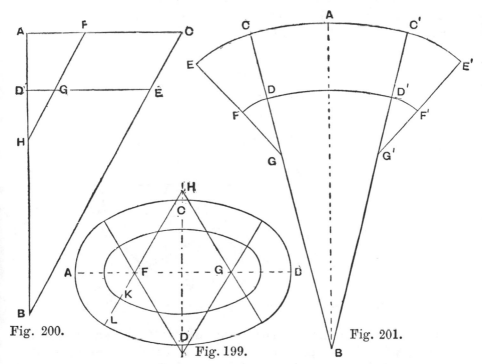

Fig. 200.

Fig. 199.

Fig. 201.

Figs. 199 to 201.—Elliptical Pan Development and Pattern.

portions of taper patterns or truncated cones. Methods of setting out conical tubes are given in Problem 37, p. 64, and one side and an end of the pan may each be regarded as portions of different conical tubes. Draw a line A B (Fig. 200), with A C at right angles. Parallel with A C, at a distance from it equal to the height of the pan, draw another line D E. Make A C equal to H L (Fig. 199), and A F (Fig. 200), equal to F L (Fig. 199). Make D E equal to H K (Fig. 199), and D G equal to F K (Fig. 199). Join F G and C E (Fig. 200), producing the lines to cut A B in H and B

respectively.   H K (Fig. 199) represents half the smaller diameter
of that conical tube of which the side of the pan is a part and
H L half the larger diameter.   To get the pattern, Fig. 201, draw a
straight line A B (shown dotted), and from B as centre, radii B C
and B E (Fig. 200), describe arcs to intersect A B.   Now from A,
with the curved length D L (Fig. 199) as radius, cut the larger
arc at C and C', and join these points to B to form the pattern for
the side.   It now needs one-half of an end pattern on each end.
Set off from C, on C B, the length of F H (Fig. 200) at G, and with
G as centre and radii equal to G C and G D draw arcs.   From C,
with length equal to A L (Fig. 199), cut the outer arc at E and

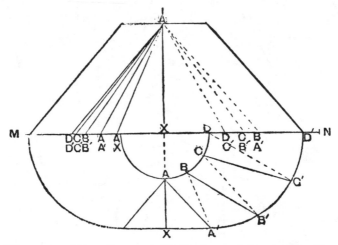

Fig. 202.—Elevation and Half-plan of Tea-bottle Top.

join E with G through F.   Deal similarly with the end C' E' F' G,
and E E' F' F is the pattern required.   If the taper of the sides
is very slight, use method 1 of Problem 37, p. 64.

To set out pattern for tea-bottle top.—In setting out the pattern
for a tea-bottle top, commence by setting out elevation and half-
plan as in Fig. 202, though for practical purposes quarter-plan
only is necessary.   The base of a tea-bottle top is straight at
the sides and semicircular at the ends ; the top is circular.   It
may be seen from Fig. 202 that the pattern is made up of a flat
triangular piece at each side, and a portion of an oblique cone
at each end.   After drawing the plan, divide each of the arcs
into any number of equal parts (here three) and join the corresponding points.   Across each segment draw a dotted line.   For

clearness the points A, B, C, etc., are marked, so that the lines in the plan may be easily found in the pattern. To get the true lengths of the plan lines, from the bottom of the vertical line A X in elevation, and on the line M N, set off on one side the plan lengths of A X, A A', B B', C C', and D D', and on the other side those of the dotted lines D C', C B', and B A'. Join all these points to the top of line A X, which represents the height of bottle top, and is at right angles to each plan length, thus giving the true length of the plan lines. To draw the pattern, Fig. 203, make the line X A at right angles to line A' A'. Make X A, Fig. 203, equal to the true length of A X, Fig. 202; also A A', Fig. 203, equal to A A', Fig. 202. Joining the points A' A' to A gives the true size of the triangular piece mentioned on p. 136. With radius A B in Fig. 202,

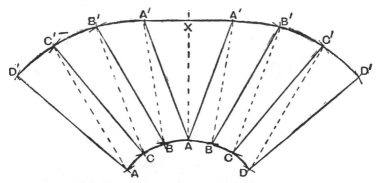

Fig. 203.—Pattern for Tea-bottle Top.

and with A, Fig. 203, as centre, describe arcs on each side at B ; and from A', radius equal to A' B' in plan, describe arcs at B'. From A', radius equal to true length of A' B (dotted line), cut the first arc at B ; and from B, radius true length of B B', cut the other arc at B'. Now join B' to B. With B' and B as centres, radii respectively equal to B' C' and B C in plan, describe arcs at C' and C, and from B', with radius true length of C B' (dotted line), cut the smaller arc at C. From C as centre, radius true length of C C', cut the other arc at C, and join C' to C. With C' and C as centres, radii respectively equal to C' D' and C D in plan, describe arcs at D' and D ; then from C', radius true length of D C' (dotted line), and from D, radius true length of D D', cut these arcs in 'D' and D ; then join D' and D. Trace an even curved line from A' through B' and C' to D', and from A through B and C to D to complete the pattern.

To set out pattern for aquarium top.—In setting out the pattern of a perforated zinc top for a square aquarium that could be taken off and put on as required, commence by drawing an elevation and plan (Figs. 204 and 205). Divide the semicircle *d d* (Fig. 205) into six equal parts, and draw lines at right angles to c c to pass through the division points *b b ;* also join the division point *c* to c and *d* to c. From any point along x y erect the

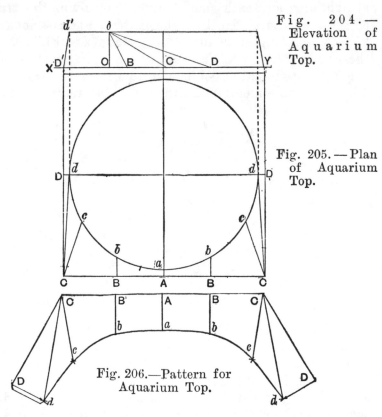

Fig. 204.— Elevation of Aquarium Top.

Fig. 205.—Plan of Aquarium Top.

Fig. 206.—Pattern for Aquarium Top.

perpendicular o o, Fig. 204, and from o mark off lengths corresponding to *b* B, *c* C, c *d* (Fig. 205) ; join these points to *o,* and the lengths found, B o, C o, D o, Fig. 204, will be the true slants of the lines *b* B, *c* C, c *d* (Fig. 205). To work the pattern, draw a line C C, Fig. 206, equal in length to C C (Fig. 205) ; mark upon this line a centre point A (Fig. 206), and mark on either side of A divisions corresponding to A B (Fig. 205). From A, B, B (Fig. 206) draw lines at right angles to C C, and mark on these lines from the point A a length equal to D′ *d′* (Fig. 204), and from B, B lengths equal to *o* B

(Fig. 204). Next use C as centre, and with radius C o (Fig. 204) draw an arc ; with $b\,c$ (Fig. 205) as radius and b (Fig. 206) as centre, cut the arc first drawn to obtain the point c ; again use C as centre on both sides of the pattern, and with radius o D (Fig. 204) draw an arc ; with the division length $c\,d$ (Fig. 205) cut the arc so as to obtain the point d. Now take the length C D (Fig. 205) as radius, and again using C (Fig. 206) as centre, draw an arc ; with D' d' (Fig. 204) as radius and d on the pattern as centre, cut the arc first drawn. Join the intersecting arcs d D by a straight line, and also join D C. Draw a curve through the intersecting arcs d, c, b, a, b, c, d, to complete the half-pattern with seams placed in the centre of the sides at D d, D d. When making the top, bend the corners C C upon any sharp-edged tools until the sides form a right angle with the end ; the semicircle forming the half top can be brought to shape by pressing the perforation to a circular shape with the thumb. If the two halves are to be grooved together, an equal allowance for the groove will be necessary on each side of the pattern ; if soldering is adopted, then one lap, as shown, will do.

To set out patterns for a coal scuttle of tapering oval section.— To set out the scuttle pattern, first draw a side elevation as shown by Fig. 207. Draw a line parallel to X Y through the centre point E to produce the points A and I at the ends. Draw projectors from A a, I i, and E e, Fig. 207, to the centre line on the plan (Fig. 208). A I (Fig. 208) will be the length of the largest complete oval section at the top of the scuttle, and $a\,i$ the length of the bottom. Mark the width of top and bottom on the vertical line E E, then draw the two ellipses to show plans of the bottom and of the section on the line A I.

Then bisect the half end curve A C of the larger oval, Fig. 208, at B, and bisect the half end curve $a\,c$ of the smaller oval at the point b. Divide the side curves C E and $c\,e$ in a similar manner, and then join each of the division points A a, B b, C c, D d, and E e by straight lines. Draw a projector from d (Fig. 208) to X Y, and from D to the section line A I (Fig. 207) ; through the points D d (Fig. 207) draw a line produced to cut the top curve of scuttle at D' ; repeat this construction for each stripe, and so place the lines B' B b and C' C c on the elevation. From the points A', B', C', and D' drop projectors to cut the produced lines, A a, B b, C c, and D d (Fig. 208) at A', B', C', and D'. A curve drawn through these points will be the plan (not true shape) of the top of the scuttle.

It will now be necessary to find the true lengths of the lines A′ *a*, B′ *b*, C′ *c*, and D′ *d* (Fig. 208). Therefore, first find the lengths A *a*, B *b*, C *c*, and D *d*, and then add the extra lengths A′ A, B′ B, C′ C,

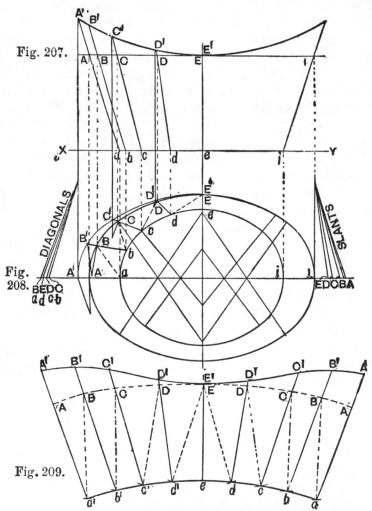

Fig. 207.

Fig. 208.

Fig. 209.

Figs. 207 to 209.—Coal-scuttle Projections and Pattern.

and D′ D separately. Draw a perpendicular at both ends of Fig. 208, and mark off on each the height E′ *e* (Fig. 207). On the base of one right angle (see right-hand side) mark off the divisions A *a*, B *b*, C *c*, D *d*, and E *e* from Fig. 207, and join them to the point which marks the height. These lengths will be the true slants of the lines A *a*, B *b*, C *c*, D *d*, and E *e* (Fig. 207). Join E *d*, D *c*, C *b*, and

B *a* as shown by dotted lines in Fig. 208. Mark these lengths on the base of the left-hand right angle, and again join to the point which marks the height; then the lengths thus produced will be the true lengths of the diagonals E *d*, D *c*, C *b*, and B *a*.

To work the pattern, Fig. 209, draw a vertical line and mark the true length of line E *e* (Fig. 207) upon it. Next take the true length of diagonal E *d* (see left hand of Fig. 208) as radius, and using E′ as centre draw an arc of a circle. With the length of division *e d* (Fig. 208) as radius, and *e* as centre, cut the arc at

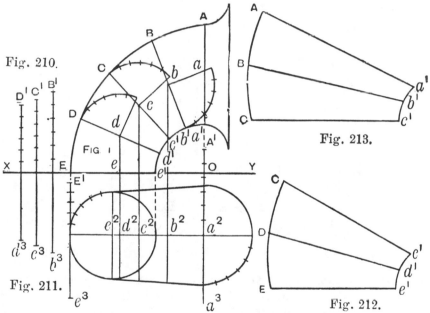

Figs. 210 to 213.—Side Elevation, Plan, and Sections of Ship's Ventilator.

points *d* and *d′*. Using *d* and *d′* as centres, and true slant D *d* as radius, draw another arc of a circle; with the division E D (Fig. 208) as radius, and E as centre, cut the last drawn arcs at points D, D (Fig. 209). Repeat this construction for each division on pattern, using the diagonals and slants in their correct order. Draw a curve through the intersecting arcs *a*, *b*, *c*, *d*, *e*, *d′*, *c′*, *b*, and *a′*, and through A, B, C, D, E, D, C, B, and A, as shown by dotted curve (Fig. 209), and join A *a*, A *a′* by straight lines. This would give the pattern as far as section line A I (Fig. 207).

To add the top part of the pattern, first find the true slant of the short lengths A' A, B' B, C' C, and D' D (Fig. 207) by taking the upright height of each line separately from the section line A I to the curved line forming top of scuttle. Transfer these heights to the perpendicular side of corresponding right angles drawn on Fig. 208 at A' A, B' B, C' C, and D' D, and join the bases of right angles to the various upright heights. The hypotenuse of each triangle so formed would be the required slants. Mark off the length of each of these slants upon the corresponding stripe upon the pattern as shown at A' A, B' B, C' C, and D' D (Fig. 209), and draw a curve through A', B', C', etc., to complete the pattern. All allowances for seams, wiring, and edging should be added to the pattern after drawing as shown.

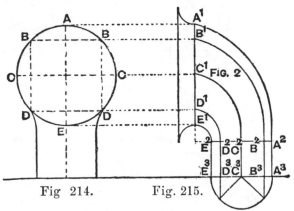

Fig 214.   Fig. 215.

Figs. 214 and 215.—Front and Side Elevations of Ship's Ventilator.

To set out pattern for ship's ventilator in four pieces. — In working the patterns for a ship's ventilator made in four pieces first draw the side elevation (Fig. 210) to the required size and shape. Then draw a line parallel to the ground line, and draw projectors from A a^1, e^1, and E to cut the line. Draw a circle with radius equal to half E e^1, and thus obtain the plan of the small end. From a^2, Fig. 211, mark a distance on each side of the centre line equal to half the diameter of the mouth A a^1, Fig. 210. By joining these points by straight lines to the diameter e^2 of the small circle a plan of the ventilator is obtained. Divide the throat curve $a^1 e^1$, Fig. 210, into any convenient number of equal parts, and divide the top curve A E into the same number of equal divisions ; straight lines which are made to join B b^1, C c^1, and D d^1 are bisected as at $a\,b\,c\,d\,e$. Draw projectors from these points to join both of the sides of the plan ; the widths across the plan would be the horizontal distance through the ventilator at the points $b\,c\,d$.　From $d\,c\,b$, Fig. 210, draw lines at right angles to the lines $D\,d^1$, $C\,c^1$, $B\,b^1$, and mark upon the line drawn from the point d a length equal to the distance from d^2, Fig. 211, to the side of the plan.　With this distance as half the minor axis, and $D\,d$ as half the major axis, draw the quarter ellipse shown; this quarter ellipse is a quarter of the true shape of a section of the ventilator upon the line $d^1\,D$.　Repeat this construction upon the lines $C\,c^1$, $B\,b^1$, taking the widths for the sections from $c^2\,b^2$ on the plan.　Then draw the additional quarter ellipses.　Divide the quarter circle which shows the true shape of the mouth of the ventilator into any suitable number of equal parts, and mark off a corresponding number of equal size along the line a^2 from a^2, Fig. 211, to A^1, Fig. 210; mark off the length $A^1\,a^2$, below a^2 to give the point a^3, then line $A^1\,a^3$ approximately equals the length

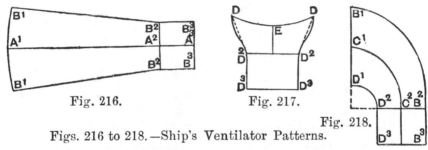

Fig. 216.　　Fig. 217.

Fig. 218.

Figs. 216 to 218.—Ship's Ventilator Patterns.

of the semi-circumference of the circle.　Repeat this working for each of the quarter sections, so as to obtain the lengths $E^1\,e^3$, $D^1\,d^3$, $C^1\,c^3$, $B^1\,b^3$ as the semi-circumference of each section.　To commence the pattern (Fig. 212) mark off along a straight line a length equal to $E^1\,e^3$; from e^1, Fig. 212, draw an arc of a circle, having the radius used for drawing the throat elevation of the ventilator.　Transfer the divisions $e^1\,d^1$, $d^1\,c^1$, Fig. 210, to the pattern for the throat curve, e^1, d^1, c^1, Fig. 212.　With d^1 as centre, and with $D^1\,d^3$ as radius, draw an arc; with $E\,D$, Fig. 210, as radius, and E, Fig. 212, as centre, cut the arc at D.　With c^1 as centre, and with $C^1\,c^3$ as radius, draw an arc; with $D\,C$, Fig. 210, as radius, and D as centre, cut the arc at C, join $D\,d^1$ and $C\,c^1$ by straight lines, and draw a curve through the intersecting arcs at $D\,C$ to complete the bottom section pattern.　The pattern for the top section, Fig. 213, is drawn in a similar way, using the length $C^1\,c^3$ as the commencing length, and then working in exactly the same way as with Fig. 212, using the lengths $B^1\,b^3$ and $A^1\,a^3$ as radius from b^1 and a^1 respectively, and cutting the arcs drawn with the division lengths C B, B A, Fig. 210, so as to obtain the intersecting arcs through which the curve A B C is drawn. Suitable allowances for lap/for riveting, etc., should be made outside the curves drawn.

To set out pattern for ship's ventilator with longitudinal seams. —For a ship's ventilator having longitudinal seams, first draw the front elevation, Fig. 214, and the side elevation, Fig. 215, and divide the mouth of ventilator into four equal parts, as B, B, D, D, Fig. 214. Draw projectors from these points to give the position of end of seams $B^1 D^1$, Fig. 215; repeat this working on semicircular plan at foot of Fig. 215, and determine the position of base end of seams as shown at $B^3 D^3$. Next draw curves to represent seams, using the throat and top curves as guides, and then draw the curve on the centre of side plate, Fig. 215, again using the outer and inner curves as guides. To draw the pattern for the top plate, mark off the length of top curve, Fig. 215, $A^1 A^2 A^3$ along a straight line, as shown at Fig. 216 by the line $A^1 A^2 A^3$, draw a line from A^3 at right angles to $A^1 A^2 A^3$, and make it equal in length to quarter circle shown in plan at foot of Fig. 215; this will give the points $B^3 B^3$. Make $B^2 B^2$ equal in length to $B^3 B^3$, and join them by a straight line parallel to $A^2 A^3$; then, with A^2 as centre and $A^1 A^2$ as radius, draw the end curve of the top pattern; make this curve at $B^1 B^1$ equal in length to quarter circle B B, Fig. 214, and join $B^1 B^2$, $B^1 B^2$ to complete the top pattern. Draw the base of throat pattern to the same dimensions as for the top pattern. Then take the length of throat curve from side pattern as radius, and, using $D^2 D^2$, Fig. 217, as centres, draw arcs of circles; make E E^2, Fig. 217, equal to $E^1 E^2$, Fig. 215, and, taking length of arc of circle from E to D, Fig. 214, as radius, and with E on pattern, Fig. 217, as centre, cut the arcs of circles already drawn at D D. Draw a curve through D E D, and join D D^2, as shown, to complete throat pattern. Draw the base for side pattern to the same dimensions as for top and throat patterns. From the point C^2 on top of rectangular base set off the curve shown on Fig. 215 at $C^1 C^2$, and from C^1 on pattern, Fig. 218, draw the line $D^1 B^1$ at right angles to $D^2 B^2$, and make it equal in length to the arc of circle D B, Fig. 214. Then, using the curve $C^1 C^2$ as a guide, draw the top curve proportionately in shape to the curve $C^1 C^2$, beginning at B^1 and ending at B^2. Draw the throat curve $D^1 D^2$ in a similar manner, to complete the pattern. The bell mouth is usually made up separately, and riveted on after the cowl is finished.

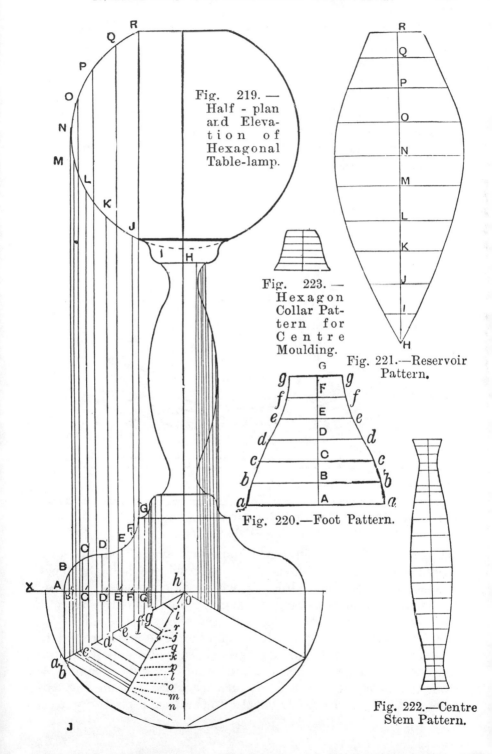

Fig. 219. — Half - plan and Elevation of Hexagonal Table-lamp.

Fig. 223. — Hexagon Collar Pattern for Centre Moulding.

Fig. 221.—Reservoir Pattern.

Fig. 220.—Foot Pattern.

Fig. 222.—Centre Stem Pattern.

To set out patterns for hexagonal table-lamp.—The patterns for an hexagonal table-lamp are obtained by first drawing an elevation of the lamp. Arrange the elevation so that when the plan is projected from it two sides of the hexagon forming the base will be at right angles to the ground line. Draw a half-plan as in Fig. 219, and from the angular points of the hexagon draw the mitre lines to the centre of the figure. Divide the curve of the foot into any convenient number of equal parts, and from each of the division points A, B, C, D, E, F, G, draw verticals to

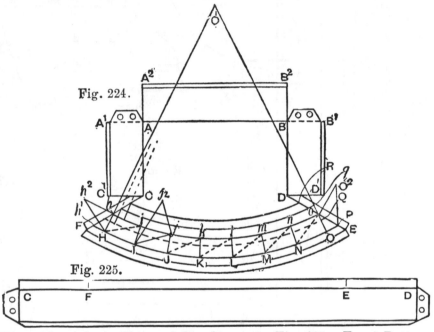

Fig. 224.—Ashpan Plan and Development: Fig. 225.—Front Pattern of Ashpan.

cut the mitre line *a o* in plan; then the length from the centre line to the mitre line of each projector will be half the length of a series of horizontal lines drawn on the moulding, and each line will contain one division point. Consequently, to work the pattern for the foot, Fig. 220, set off upon a straight line divisions corresponding in size and number to those round the moulding as A, B, C, D, E, F, G; through each division point draw lines at right angles to the line A G; then take the distance A *a* from the plan and mark it off on each side of A on Fig. 220; transfer the distance B' *b*, Fig. 219, to the line B on the pattern,

Fig. 220, and repeat this process for each line; this would give the points *a a*, *b b*, *c c*, *d d*, *e e*, *f f*, *g g* on the pattern. A curve should now be drawn through these points to complete the pattern for the base. The pattern for the reservoir, Fig. 221, is worked in the same way; the letters H to R indicate the divisions which are to be transferred to the centre line of the pattern, and the widths to be marked on the lines drawn at right angles to H R, Fig. 221, are shown by the lengths measured from the points on the centre line (indicated by italics corresponding to the letters on the elevation) to the mitre line on the second face of the hexagon forming the plan. Fig. 222 is the pattern for the centre stem of the lamp, and Fig. 223 the small

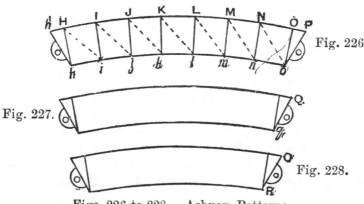

Figs. 226 to 228.—Ashpan Patterns.

hexagonal collars to fit the top and bottom of Fig. 222. To fit the pieces together, first cut out a template to the shape shown by the elevation, and bend each section exactly to fit this template; then file the edges lightly where necessary, and a neat mitred seam will result.

To set out patterns for ashpan.—To set out the patterns for an ashpan having conical brass steps first draw a plan of the pan, as shown by A B D E F C, Fig. 224. Then produce the lines C A, A B, and B D, and draw C C¹, A A¹, A A², B B¹, B B², and D D¹ equal in length to the depth of the pan. Mark an allowance for laps to be bent round on the back of the pan for riveting, as shown at A A¹, B B¹, and make an allowance along the lines C¹ A¹, A² B², and B¹ D¹ for folding over, so as to stiffen the sides and end. Also make a suitable allowance along the sides of the front from D to E, E to F, and F to C, for a paned down seam,

and then notch the corners F E as shown ; this will give the pattern
for the pan without the front.   For the front draw a rectangle,
in length equal to the distance round the curved front from F to E,
with the lengths F C, D E (see Fig. 225) added, and in depth equal
to A A^1, Fig. 224 ; make suitable allowances for riveting at the
ends C D, and for wiring and edging, as shown on Fig. 225.   Draw
the plans of each of the conical steps $h\,h^1$, Q q, R o, in their proper
positions, using the centre (o^1) of the curved front of the pan.
These arcs will represent plans of parts of frustums of right
cones, and the method of developing the surface will be identical
for each step.   The pattern for the first step o P, $h\,h^1$, Fig. 224,
is worked as follows : Join o and h to the centre o^1, and produce both lines to cut the outer arc at H and o.   Divide this
arc into any convenient number of divisions, H, I, J, etc., and
also divide the inner arc, or top of first step, into a similar
number of equal divisions as h, i, j, etc.   Join I i, J j, K k, etc.,
by straight lines, and also join H i, I j, J k, etc., by dotted lines
as shown.   The first drawn lines will be the plans of true slants
on the conical surface, and the dotted lines plans of diagonals on
the same surface.   Draw lines at right angles to H h and I j, and
mark at $h^2 j^2$ a length equal to the depth of the pan.   Join h^2 to
H, and this length will be the slant of the frustum.   Then join
I to j^2 ; this length will be the diagonal slant.   Now draw a
straight line H h, Fig. 226, and mark the slant length H h^2 upon
it.   Now with the diagonal slant I j^2 as radius, and H as centre,
draw an arc at i.   With the division length $h\,i$, Fig. 224, as
radius, and h, Fig. 226, as centre, cut the arc first drawn at i.
Again using the slant H h as radius, and i as centre, draw an arc
at I ; and with the outer division length H I, Fig. 224, as radius,
and H as centre, draw an arc to cut the arc first drawn at I.
Repeat this construction, using the true slants and diagonals
alternately for the remaining divisions.   Draw a curve through
the points H, I, J, etc., and through h, i, j, etc., to form the top
and bottom of the pattern.   It may be seen from the plan that
the pattern as drawn does not include the small triangular-shaped
pieces shown at H $h\,h^1$ and on the opposite end.   To add these,
first draw a line at right angles to o P, Fig. 224, and mark at o^2
the height of the other triangles.   Join o^2 P, and this length will
be the true slant of o P.   Using this length as radius, and o
and h, Fig. 226, as centres, describe arcs.   Now with o P as
radius, Fig. 224, and H and o, Fig. 226, as centres, describe arcs

to cut those first drawn at P and h^1. Join these points, and make allowances on the ends for riveting, as shown, to complete the pattern. Figs. 227 and 228 are worked by precisely the same method; the length of the curves Q q, R O corresponding to the lengths of the curves Q q, R o, Fig. 224.

To set out patterns for oblong back-warmer.—In working the patterns for an oblong back-warmer with perpendicular sides and taper ends, begin by drawing a side elevation of the warmer, as shown by the curves ending at A B D C (Fig. 229). Next join A C by a straight line, and draw a line parallel to A C through the

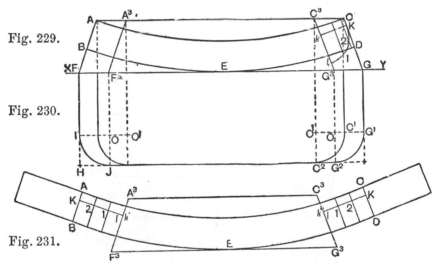

Fig. 229.

Fig. 230.

Fig. 231.

Figs. 229 to 231.—Projections and Pattern of Oblong Back-warmer.

centre of the curve B D at E. Produce the lines A B and C D to cut X Y at F and G. The lines that enclose the side view of the warmer may be assumed to represent a side elevation of a rectangular-shaped body, with rounded corners, whose sides and ends contain the sides and ends of the warmer. For a semi-plan (Fig. 230), draw a line parallel to the ground line, and at a distance from it equal to half the width of the warmer. Drop lines perpendicular to the ground line from F and G, and from A and C, to cut the line first drawn. Mark from the corner H (Fig. 230) equal lengths (proportionate to the arc of the curve required) at I and J. Use the same length as radius, and with centres I and J describe arcs intersecting at O. Use O as centre, and draw the quadrant required. Repeat this construction for the corners of the top, of which o¹ is centre. Next draw perpendiculars from G^2 to x y, and from c^2 to A c (Fig. 229). Join c^3 and G^3, to show on the elevation where the flat side and the curved corner meet. Set off a line k K at right angles to c^3 G^3, and mark from k along c^3 G^3 a length equal to the radius of the corners on plan. Use this length $k\,l$ as half the length, and k K as half the width of an ellipse, and draw the quarter ellipse shown. This shows the true shape of a section of the corner when cut by an inclined plane passing through it at K k, and at right angles to c^3 G^3. Divide the quarter ellipse into any suitable

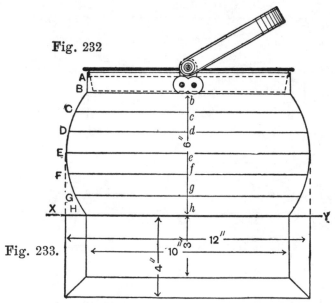

Figs. 232 and 233.—Side Elevation and Half-plan of Fishing-can.

number of equal divisions, as l, 1, 2, K, and through each division point draw lines parallel to c G as shown. To draw the pattern, Fig. 231, commence by reproducing the part of the side elevation shown between the lines A^3 F^3 and c^3 G^3 (Fig. 229), with the curves that form the side in position. Upon either end mark distances equal to the length c^3 k (Fig. 229), and from these points k' and k'' draw lines at right angles to A^3 F^3 and c^3 G^3 (Fig. 231). Along these lines set off a number of divisions corresponding to those shown on the quarter ellipse (Fig. 229), as 1, 2, K. Through these points draw lines parallel to A^3 F^3 and c^3 G^3. Measure the lengths of the lines through k, 1, 2, K in Fig. 229, from the line K k to where they cut the top curve on the side elevation of the warmer, and transfer these distances to the stripes on Fig. 231 with the corresponding letters or numbers upon the pattern. Take also the lengths from K k to the lower curve, and transfer them to the stripes on the pattern. Draw a curve through the points found, and this curve would be the pattern for the corners added to that for the side. Draw lines at right angles to A B and C D, and make them equal in length to G′ G (Fig. 230). Join the points found by straight lines to complete the pattern for one half of the warmer when the seam is to be formed at the centre of the ends. Suitable allowances for the seam should be made on the ends.

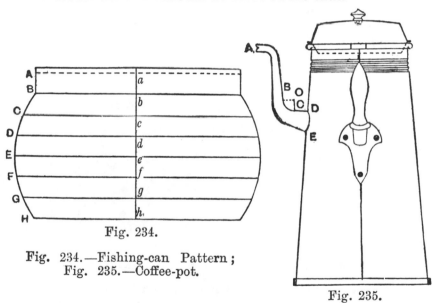

Fig. 234.

Fig. 234.—Fishing-can Pattern ;
Fig. 235.—Coffee-pot.

Fig. 235.

To set out pattern for fishing-can.—In setting out the pattern for a fishing-can it is necessary to first draw a side elevation and half-plan of the can to the required sizes, as shown by Figs. 232 and 233. Then divide the end curve into any suitable number of equal divisions, B, C, D, E, F, G, and H, Fig. 232 ; from these points draw lines parallel to the ground line as shown. For the pattern of the side, draw a vertical line as $a\,h$, Fig. 234, then take the distance A B, Fig. 232, and mark from a to b, Fig. 234, and from b to h mark off a number of divisions equal to those shown from B to H, Fig. 232. Then through the division points a, b, c, d, e, f, g, h, Fig. 234, draw a series of lines at right angles to $a\,h$; then take the distance B b, Fig. 232, and mark off the points A B, Fig. 234. Now transfer the lengths C c, D d, E e, F f, G g, H h, Fig. 232, to the lines with the corresponding letters on Fig. 234, to determine the points C, D, E, F, G, H on the pattern. Draw a curve through these points as shown, join B A by a straight line, and make an allowance for a fold above the dotted line to complete the side pattern. For the end pattern draw a rectangle equal in length to a h, Fig. 234, and 6 in. wide, and add curves on the long sides corresponding to those at the end of the side pattern. The bottom pattern would be a rectangle 10 in. by 6 in., with a small allowance on each side for

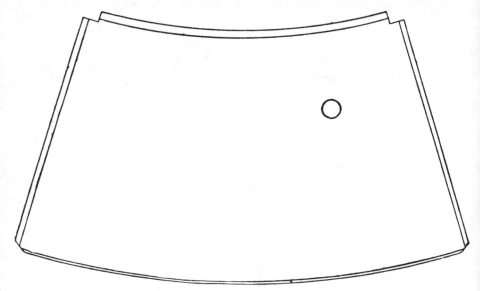

Fig. 236.—Body-plan of Coffee-pot.

turning up; the cover would also be a rectangle of the same dimensions as the bottom, but with an extra allowance for edging, so that the rim may be paned on.

To set out patterns for a coffee-pot.—A coffee-pot (Fig. 235) to hold about three pints would measure at the top $3\frac{1}{4}$ in. in diameter, $4\frac{1}{2}$ in. in diameter at the bottom, and its height on the slant would be 8 in. The body pattern is a frustum of a cone, and is developed by the method given on page 64. At one-quarter the distance round the cone mark the position of the spout hole, and make allowances for wiring, edging, and grooving, as shown by Fig. 236. To form the spout pattern approximately, draw two lines at right angles, as at Fig. 237, making the horizontal line A equal in length to the circumference of the mouth of the spout, A, Fig. 235, and the width from B to B, Fig. 237, equal to the circumference at B, Fig. 235. Draw the quarter circles B O C, Fig. 237, with the same radius as shown on Fig. 235, and draw horizontal lines from C to D equal to C D, Fig. 235 ; drop perpendiculars from D D, making them equal to the semi-circumference of the end of the spout. Then from E draw a line at the same inclination to E D as the lower line of the spout makes with the end of D E, Fig. 235, and produce these lines on each side of the pattern to meet at the centre line in

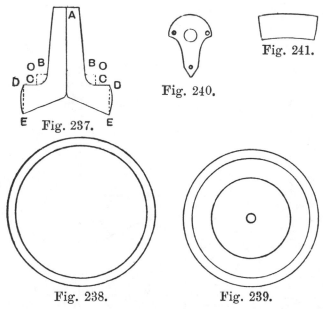

Fig. 241.

Fig. 240.

Fig. 237.

Fig. 238.   Fig. 239.

Figs. 237 to 239.—Coffee-pot Patterns ; Fig. 240.—Socket-plate for Coffee-pot Handle ; Fig. 241.—Conical Socket of Coffee-pot.

Fig. 237 ; notch the pattern slightly, and it is then complete. Figs. 238 and 239 are the patterns for bottom and top respectively ; on the former allow for edging, and on Fig. 239 allow for both hollowing and edging. Fig. 240 is the handle socket plate, and Fig. 241 the conical socket, the pattern for this being obtained by the method used for the body.

To set out patterns for an oval kettle.—In setting out the patterns of an oval kettle, Fig. 242, to hold 1½ gallons, first assume a proportionate length and width for the bottom, then a height suitable to the capacity required can be readily determined.   One and a half gallons contains 415·875 cubic inches; divide this by the number of square inches in the bottom of the kettle, and the quotient will be the height required.   If the bottom of the kettle is assumed to be

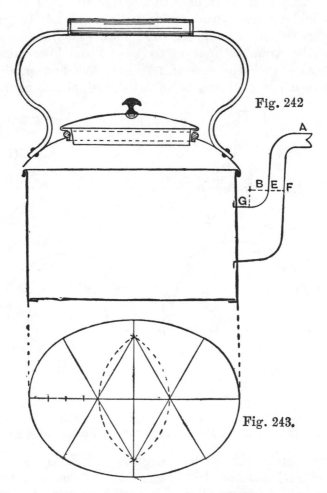

Fig. 242

Fig. 243.

Fig. 242.—Oval Kettle; Fig. 243.—Oval Kettle Bottom Pattern.

10·5 in. long and 7·75 in. wide, the working will be as follows :
$$\frac{415 \cdot 875}{10 \cdot 5 \times 7 \cdot 75 \times \cdot 7854} = 6 \cdot 56,$$ the required height in inches for the body of the kettle.   Determine the circumference of the oval by first finding the circumference of a circle whose diameter is equal to half the combined length and width of the oval,

thus : $\dfrac{10\cdot5 + 7\cdot75}{2} = 9\frac{1}{8}$, $9\frac{1}{8} \times 3\frac{1}{7} = 28\frac{3}{4}$, the circumference of the oval. The body pattern, Fig. 244, is a rectangle $28\frac{3}{4}$ in. long

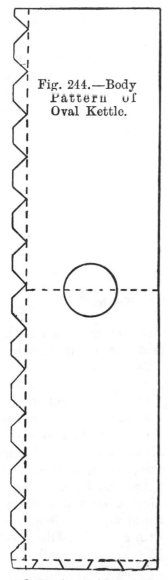

Fig. 244.—Body Pattern of Oval Kettle.

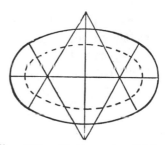

Fig. 246.—Pattern for Lid of Oval Kettle.

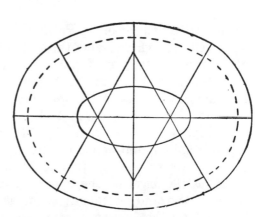

Fig. 245.—Pattern for Top of Kettle.

and $7\frac{1}{4}$ in. wide ; $\frac{3}{4}$ in. extra in depth is allowed for forming cramps to hold the bottom in position when brazing. To draw the oval for the bottom employ the method illustrated by Fig. 31 and described on page 42. The constructional lines of the oval are shown in Fig. 243.   Set out the pattern for the top, Fig. 245, in exactly the same manner, making an allowance for hollowing and edging, as indicated by the dotted lines.   Mark centrally the length of the opening for the cover, and, using the same centres, describe the arcs required to form the inner oval, Fig. 245.   The pattern for the lid, Fig. 246, is also drawn by the same method.   The inner dotted oval, Fig. 246, is the same size as the inner oval in Fig. 245 ; sufficient allowance is made for the lap over the rim flange and also for hollowing.   To set out the spout pattern approximately correct, draw a line, Fig. 247, and set off A H C D equal in length to the circumference of the

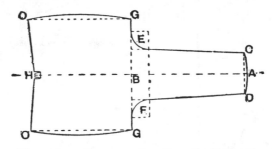

Fig. 247.—Pattern for Spout of Kettle.

small end of the spout.   From A to B, Fig. 247, mark a length, equal A to B, Fig. 242, and through B draw a line at right angles. Make the length E F, Fig. 247, equal to the circumference E F, Fig. 242, and then draw the quarter circles at E and F, using the same radius as shown on Fig. 242.   Draw G C equal to the straight length from curve to body on the inside of the spout at G, Fig. 242.   From G G, Fig. 247, mark lengths to O O equal to the semi-circumference of the spout at the largest end.   Join these points to the centre line at H, sloping them at the same angle as the base of the spout.   Notch the centre, and cut a cramp at top and bottom of seam, as indicated on the diagram. The rim for the lid is a narrow strip of metal equal in length to the circumference of the hole, Fig. 245, with a suitable allowance for lap at the seam.

INDEX.

PRINTED BY CASSELL & CO., LTD., LUDGATE HILL, LONDON, E.C.

20.1008